PTSD and Relationships

Loving Someone With PTSD

Tim L. Gardner

advice. The content within this book has been derived from various sources. Please consult a licensed professional before attempting any techniques outlined in this book.

By reading this document, the reader agrees that under no circumstances is the author responsible for any losses, direct or indirect, that are incurred as a result of the use of the information contained within this document, including, but not limited to, errors, omissions, or inaccuracies.

Table of Contents

Introduction

"Relationships don't last because of the good times; they last because the hard times were handled with love and care."

—*Anmol Andore*

Post-traumatic stress disorder, or PTSD, is a severe and devastating condition. Many individuals end up facing this issue after experiencing or witnessing traumas like war, accidents, sexual assault, kidnapping, and many more.

Many people end up suffering trauma at some point—studies show that 70 percent of adults experience at least one traumatic event in their lives. What's more, 20 percent of the people who experience trauma will end up with PTSD.

This condition is one that should not be overlooked, because it affects every aspect of an individual's life—from their health down to their relationships. If you are in a relationship with someone who has PTSD, you likely already know that it can be extremely complicated and frustrating. In fact, many relationships end due to this condition.

To gain a better understanding of this impact, take a look at the following stats:

- In the initial weeks and months after a trauma, survivors may feel detached, angry, and uncomfortable in their relationships. Many of them can get over this phase and go back to the previous state of closeness and intimacy in their relationships. However, the five to 10% of survivors who end up with PTSD may have issues maintaining relationships.
- People with PTSD often struggle with work and other daily activities. This may also have an influence on the higher rates of unemployment and divorce. Combat veterans who have been diagnosed with this condition have reported difficulties in their marital lives. Studies show that almost 50 percent of their marriages end up in divorce—in some cases, they may have more than one marriage end the same way.

Today, tons of relationships and families suffer because of a loved one's PTSD. This is primarily because many people don't know the steps to take to help their loved ones recover from the experience. If someone you love has PTSD, this is not the end of the world. This condition can be treated with the right knowledge, but you need to start taking steps today.

Many people have taken the wrong step by trying to sort this problem out by themselves only to watch things get worse and, in some cases, end up losing the relationship they are trying to save. In purchasing this book, you have already made a bold and strategic move in the right direction.

This book is your one-stop-shop for all the information you need regarding PTSD, how it affects your relationship, and more. In this book, you will also learn some of the following:

- The causes and symptoms of post-traumatic stress disorder.
- How to ensure you don't develop caregiver burden.
- The various forms of treatment available.
- How to properly communicate with your loved one who has PTSD.
- How to offer your loved one the right support.

All of this and more will be covered in detail within this book. PTSD can ruin lives and relationships if left untreated. If your loved one develops this condition and you don't take the right steps, you can slowly watch them change from the happy person they used to be into a shadow of their former selves. This is something you could be stuck with for the remainder of your lives, and I am confident this is not what you want.

To make sure this is not your story, it's important to help your loved one get treatment now—and for you to educate yourself about the condition, too. This is not something to be postponed until you are ready. The longer you leave your loved one with this condition, the harder it will be to save your relationship. In fact, it could lead to the relationship's end.

I have witnessed what PTSD can do to a person and their relationships. My sister had this problem for an extremely long time after surviving a toxic and abusive relationship. She was still able to manage it, but when I was through with my business degree and opened up my coffee shop, her condition worsened.

She soon started to withdraw from everyone, including me. She was always on edge and stopped doing the things she loved. Some days, all it took was something extremely minor to trigger her to blow up in anger. We all looked for ways to help her, but there was no solution coming forth. Then, one day, she had her usual outburst in front of my kids and hers, and I could see they were really scared of her. I knew that if this continued, she was going to lose everybody around her.

At that point, I decided to take action and intensify my search for a solution. I explained my decision to my wife, who was understanding and happy to provide me with the help I needed. With her support, I took up a part-time psychology degree online. By combining the knowledge I learned with my degree, interaction with other PTSD sufferers, and numerous support networks I created over the years, I was able to help save my sister from the claws of this dangerous condition.

It took a whole two years for her to get a hold of her life again. However, it was a fulfilling experience for every one of us involved. Getting my degree took me two years, and saving my sister took another two years. This, in addition to the extra five years I spent doing in-depth research on this condition and interacting with others who have experienced it, has made me a specialist in this field.

Believe me when I say that I know just how much PTSD can make a person lose. I did all of this so I could have a better understanding of the condition and ensure nobody else has to see their loved one go through what my sister did. With all of my experience, I have helped numerous individuals regain control of their lives and relationships, and I want to help even more people. This is why I have collected all of the experiences I've accumulated into this book.

You and your loved one deserve to be together. You shouldn't have to lose your relationship because of PTSD. You deserve happiness, and you can help them get through this condition while maintaining your relationship. Treatment is available for PTSD—a study supports this by proving that no less than 46 percent of the people who have PTSD saw improvements in the first six weeks after they began psychotherapy. What's more, researchers have also stated that 62 percent of people who are on medication see improvements.

In all honesty, PTSD is a scary thing to face. Even if you or your loved one don't have it, you can educate yourself on all of the symptoms associated with this condition so you can help someone in need down the line.

If you are serious about ending the hold PTSD has on your loved one and your relationship, then read on.

Chapter 1:

What is PTSD?

Post-traumatic stress disorder, or PTSD, is a severe and devastating condition people develop after experiencing a trauma or life-threatening event. Initially, this condition came to light after World War I, when it was diagnosed in soldiers who returned from battle.

At that point, it was known as shell-shock, but as scientists uncovered more knowledge of the brain and how it responds to extremely stressful circumstances, the condition was linked to other sources of trauma in addition to combat. Now, many individuals suffer from this condition—even if they've never been to war.

In some cases, the condition resolves itself, but the majority of those who develop it may need treatment from experienced professionals if they want to ever free themselves of the condition and function normally.

Some events that could result in PTSD range from domestic abuse, war, child abuse, rape, and many others. We will be looking into all of this in detail below.

Causes of PTSD

When an individual is exposed to a traumatic event that poses a danger to them, it may result in PTSD. However, there are also instances where the person does not have to experience the trauma themselves— they could witness it happening to a loved one.

A few examples of situations and experiences that can cause this problem include:

Military Combat

As previously stated, this is a prevalent cause of PTSD. It was initially known as shell-shock or battle fatigue as soldiers who arrived home after the war were some of the first groups of people to experience PTSD symptoms.

In fact, more than half of the veterans who fought in Vietnam are known to suffer from this condition.

This is mostly due to the deaths of comrades by gunshots, ambushes, bomb blasts, and so on. The sheer number of traumatic events associated with combat makes this one of the easiest ways for anyone to develop PTSD.

Car Accidents

Car accidents happen all the time. However, some are worse than others and can leave a different impact on the individuals involved. Being hit by another vehicle, hitting a person, or an extremely traumatic collision can easily trigger PTSD.

For instance, Mark regularly drove 3,000 miles each week, and it was never an issue. But one day, he was driving with his wife and kids when a truck rammed into his vehicle, instantly killing his wife and leaving him in the hospital for weeks.

When Mark recovered, driving became a tedious event. Anytime he was on the road, he kept seeing a truck ramming into him, and this forced him to frequently stop the car even though there was no imminent danger. Soon, he couldn't drive anymore and was constantly plagued with flashbacks and nightmares. These made him experience sleepless nights and depression, along with other PTSD symptoms.

This is a typical example of how car accidents can trigger PTSD, and most are only able to overcome it if they seek the right treatment.

Sexual Assault and Rape

Rape is also another common reason for PTSD symptoms, especially in women. The Centers for

Disease Control and Prevention (CDC) states that almost one of every five women in the United States are sexually assaulted or raped at some point in their lives—usually by a person they know and trust. This figure is even higher in some other countries. However, sexual assault can be experienced by boys and men, too.

Irrespective of the gender of the person involved, sexual violence can be very damaging. In addition to the physical injuries it may leave behind, there are also mental damages, which is usually what triggers PTSD symptoms.

Victims can feel broken, alone, ashamed, and scared while battling with frequent flashbacks and nightmares. It can change the overall outlook of an individual as they may begin to see the world and their immediate environment as unsafe. It becomes almost impossible to trust others, and they begin to question their self-worth, sense or judgment, and themselves.

Many victims of sexual assault tend to blame themselves for what happened. They are also unable to enjoy a healthy relationship because of their experience, as they see intimacy as being vulnerable and risky. What's more, many survivors of rape may battle with PTSD symptoms alongside depression and anxiety.

In most cases, the symptoms could last for months, and sometimes years after the occurrence. This could lead to victims avoiding any locations or people that they associate with the trauma.

Experiencing War

Individuals residing in countries torn by war may also develop PTSD. This is seen in adults right down to kids. They experience all of the horrible events trained soldiers do and may end up dealing with PTSD symptoms for an extended part of their lives.

Burning buildings, bomb runs, violent assault, starvation, and many other things that are responsible for the deaths of numerous individuals in war all have a direct link to PTSD.

Seeing your loved one or someone you know die is hard enough, but seeing them die in any of the manners listed above is enough to give any person constant nightmares, flashbacks, and other PTSD symptoms.

Experiencing or Witnessing Violence

Paul lived a happy life in a small town—he'd never experienced any sort of violence, except what he saw on television. However, one normal day at work, a disgruntled ex-employee came in with a high-caliber rifle and started shooting. He watched in horror as many of the people he worked with each day fell down dead after being hit. He saw the blood splash everywhere as he hid, terrified, under his desk.

He felt a cold, sharp pain on his shoulder, and that was all he remembered, only to wake up in the hospital.

When his brain pieced it together, his life was never the same again. The vivid memories from his near-death experience are enough to trigger PTSD symptoms years later.

Numerous individuals who lived in Manhattan on September 11, 2001, close to the twin towers, have experienced PTSD. The same would be the case of anyone who experienced events similar to the above, like muggings, assaults, or kidnappings.

Natural Disasters

Natural disasters like earthquakes, floods, tornadoes, and hurricanes are all linked to PTSD. All of these can happen unexpectedly, and victims are often unable to escape or prepare. This could lead to loss of property, near-death experience, loss of loved ones, and feelings of helplessness linked with PTSD symptoms.

Some people witness all of the destruction firsthand and are left battling to survive. If they do survive, all of the death and destruction they've witnessed can have a lasting impact on their lives and may trigger PTSD symptoms.

However, the length, severity, and how close you were to the trauma all have an influence on whether you experience PTSD symptoms. If you experience severe trauma like sexual assault, war, or natural disasters, you face a higher probability of getting PTSD compared to someone who witnesses a kidnapping or car accident.

PTSD Risk Factors

Since everyone who experiences a trauma does not end up with PTSD, there is ongoing research to better pinpoint who has a higher possibility of ending up with the condition. This is to ensure that treatments and interventions can provide the best results.

It is impossible to determine who will develop PTSD after experiencing trauma and those who won't. But the following are a few risk factors that may contribute to it:

Genetics

There is still ongoing research on the role of genetics in PTSD development. Numerous studies have shown the influence of genetics on the development of conditions related to mental illness, like bipolar disorder, schizophrenia, and major depressive disorder. Also, researchers have started to find a genetic influence on PTSD development.

Women have a higher probability of developing PTSD than men. PTSD has been observed to occur in 10 to 12 percent of women as opposed to five to six percent of men. Researchers have also discovered that, particularly in European-American females, close to 29 percent of the possibility of experiencing PTSD after dealing with trauma was due to the influence of genetic factors. The genetic possibility was observed to be less in males.

Individuals with paranoid, dependent, and antisocial traits tend to react more emotionally than others in stressful situations. It also takes them more time to recover from a negative situation, which puts them more at risk of suffering PTSD symptoms.

Current Research

Presently, genetic markers are being investigated for the role they play in aiding PTSD development. They range from those like the serotonin transporter gene, and those that have to do with the hypothalamic-pituitary-adrenal axis.

Societal Factors

The availability of social support or the absence of it is a very important risk factor. Individuals who don't have broad options when it comes to social support have a higher likelihood of developing PTSD. Once the traumatic event is over, having a safe support network is crucial to aid people in processing their experiences in a healthy way. A good support system will also help to establish hope and trust in the world once more.

What's more, individuals who depend on avoidant coping techniques will be less able to find healthy connections or use a support network after dealing with trauma. However, people who take this route and try to handle their trauma by being alone may be more likely to develop symptoms of PTSD.

Even individuals with the right level of support may still have problems getting over PTSD with ease, so the situation is worse for those who choose isolation as an option.

Neurological and Biological Factors

Neuroticism and IQ have been shown to have a possible influence on the likelihood of developing PTSD after dealing with trauma. Those who tend to receive lower scores in IQ tests have proven to be more likely to experience PTSD.

Neuroticism is a personality trait in individuals who have a higher than average possibility of experiencing fear, anger, feelings of guilt, sadness, and frustration.

PTSD, alongside other conditions like depression, has been linked with reduced brain volume, especially in the prefrontal areas of the brain. According to research, this reduction in volume was linked to increased self-reports of anxiety from contributors.

Other Factors

Past trauma is another common risk factor in PTSD development. The effect of trauma has been observed to have a snowballing effect. This implies that a trauma survivor who showed no prior PTSD symptoms may develop symptoms after another trauma.

If a person has an external locus of control (that is where they believe that everything that happens to them stems from external factors that they have no control over, like bias, injustice, or luck), they are more likely to have a hard time coping with stress. In turn, this enhances their susceptibility to trauma.

Another risk factor includes life stressors. There are many stressful events one can go through in life. Depending on the individual, these events can increase the likelihood of developing PTSD. Some of these include divorce, loss of a loved one, or job loss.

There are instances where seemingly positive life events could trigger it as well, like the birth of a new child.

The nature of the event that triggers the PTSD is also something to consider as an influential element. It has been proven that more serious events—like witnessing death or severe violence, especially involving a loved one, or suffering an injury during a trauma—could be a major risk factor.

Additionally, when a person suffers physical pain due to their trauma, like what one would experience from rape, sexual abuse, or long-term domestic violence, the likelihood of developing PTSD can be higher. This is because physical pain tends to remind the victim of the trauma.

People who have a history of other mental conditions, like anxiety, depression, and bipolar disorder, are more likely to develop PTSD after experiencing a trauma. The same is also the case if they have a close relative dealing with symptoms like depression.

If you have PTSD, you are more susceptible to other mental conditions like eating disorders, depression, alcohol and substance abuse, etc. This means it is essential that you seek treatment if you are battling with PTSD, for your own sake.

Depending on the trauma they experienced, PTSD symptoms may affect people differently. However, if you find yourself or someone you know is unable to properly complete daily activities, it's time to get help.

Types of PTSD

After a PTSD diagnosis, precise specifics may be pointed out—unique features that make this particular case unique from a broad PTSD diagnosis.

These specifics are:

Preschool

There are precise PTSD symptoms for kids six years and under. As kids live through or witness traumatic events, they can experience symptoms that are emotionally distressing. Similar to adults, there are a few criteria a young child needs to meet to be diagnosed with PTSD.

Dissociative

This specifier in PTSD diagnoses has to do with the presence of constant or persistent symptoms of derealization or depersonalization. Depersonalization implies that a person is going through an event that is happening to them as though they are witnessing it instead of experiencing it themselves.

Derealization means someone is feeling things around them like they are not real. It is almost like the person is not connected to the world and the environment around them.

Delayed Expression

This was previously referred to as delayed onset before it was replaced with delayed expression in the DSM-5. Even though individuals with this specifier meet the criteria for PTSD, it is not completely met until six months have passed since the trauma.

An individual could start to experience some of the symptoms faster than others. However, they won't meet the criteria for diagnosis until they have gotten to the six-month target.

Complex

There are instances where individuals can suffer from solitary or acute cases of trauma, like a robbery at gunpoint, a mugging, or an accident. These are categorized as acute because they have a lower probability of becoming repetitive experiences.

There are other kinds of traumatic events that can be more repetitive, like sexual abuse, domestic violence, or childhood abandonment—the individual tends to suffer this event repeatedly over time. Individuals who have suffered these forms of chronic trauma may develop symptoms of PTSD.

PTSD Diagnosis

A medical expert will be responsible for diagnosing PTSD. This diagnosis will be dependent on the psychological evaluation of the signs and symptoms you are experiencing.

To be medically diagnosed with this condition, you will need to meet the criteria stated in the fifth edition of the Diagnostic and Statistical Manual of Mental Disorders published by the American Psychological Association.

Criterion A

You were exposed to one event or more that threatened severe injury, sexual violation, or death. Also, these events were experienced in one or more of the ways below:

- You directly experienced the event
- You were present as the incident occurred to another person
- You were repeatedly exposed to worrying event details, like a priest always hearing vivid confessions from criminals
- You found out about an event where a friend or loved one experienced death, violence, or was threatened with death

Criterion B

You experience no fewer than one of the intrusive symptoms linked with a traumatic event:

- Expected or unforeseen repetitive, invasive, and involuntary disturbing memories of trauma
- Continuous disturbing dreams where the dream content has to do with the traumatic event
- Powerful and persistent distress when exposed to external or internal cues that are linked to your trauma

- Experiencing some form of dissociation like flashbacks, where you feel like the traumatic event is occurring once more
- Powerful reactions in the body when exposed to something that reminds you of the traumatic event

Criterion C

Regular avoidance of reminders linked with the traumatic event as shown by any of the following:

- Avoidance of places, individuals, objects, situations, or conversations that bring up memories of the trauma
- Avoidance of physical sensations, feelings, and thoughts that bring up memories of the trauma

Criterion D

No fewer than two of the negative changes in mood and thoughts that cropped up or became worse after experiencing the trauma:

- The inability to remember crucial aspects of the trauma
- Constant increasing negative assessments of others, yourself, and the world
- Persistent negative emotional states like fear, anger, or shame

- Inability to experience positive emotions like love, happiness, and joy
- Increase in the blame of others or self-blame about the reason for a traumatic event and the implication
- Loss of interest in previous hobbies and activities
- A feeling of detachment from others

Criterion E

No fewer than two of the changes below in arousal that became worse or started after experiencing trauma:

- Self-destructive or impulsive behavior
- Aggressive behavior
- Hypervigilance or always feeling on guard like there is danger around, even when nothing is there
- Issues sleeping
- Increased startle response

Criterion F

The symptoms above persist beyond one month.

Criterion G

The symptoms affect various aspects of your life while causing you significant distress.

Criterion H

The symptoms are not a result of a medical condition or substance use.

DSM-5 PTSD Diagnosis

To be diagnosed with PTSD as stated by the DSM-5, the following are the criteria you will need to meet:

- Criterion A
- Criterion B: One symptom or more
- Criterion C: One symptom or more
- Criterion D: Two symptoms or more
- Criterion E: Two symptoms or more
- Criteria F through H

Obviously, you don't need to have all of the symptoms listed above. There is hardly a person with PTSD who experiences each of the related symptoms.

For diagnoses to be assessed, there are also additional requirements like:

- How long have you been dealing with your symptoms?
- How have you responded to the trauma?
- How much have the symptoms interfered with your life?

To get the right result, a qualified expert needs to review all of these.

Why Does PTSD Develop?

There is no precise reason as to why people develop the condition. However, there are a few possible suggestions.

Survival Mechanisms

A popular theory as to why one experiences PTSD symptoms is due to the natural survival mechanism built into humans to help us deal with trauma.

For instance, the feeling of always being on edge may arise to help you react quickly if another crisis occurs. Flashbacks may urge you to analyze the event critically, so you are ready if the event springs up once more. Nightmares can also help you relive the event in a similar way, so you can spot details you missed the first time and better protect yourself if it happens again.

However, even though all of these mechanisms intend to protect you, they do the opposite. This is because they prevent you from processing the traumatic event and moving past it.

High Levels of Adrenaline

According to studies, individuals experiencing PTSD don't have a normal level of stress hormones. Under normal circumstances, when the body is in danger, it creates stress hormones like adrenaline as a means of urging the body to respond.

This response is called the "fight-or-flight" reaction, and it aids in dampening the senses and dulling pain. Individuals with PTSD have been observed to develop fight-or-flight hormones in high amounts, even when there is no danger.

It is presumed that this may be the cause of the constant feeling of being on edge and the deadened emotions some people with PTSD experience.

Brain Alterations

When brain scans were carried out on people with PTSD, the area of the brain that had to do with the processing of emotions shows up differently.

The hippocampus, which controls emotions and memory, has been shown to have a smaller size in individuals who have PTSD. It is presumed that changes in this part of the brain may be linked with memory issues, anxiety, fear, and flashbacks. When the hippocampus does not function as it should, it may lead to nightmares processed the wrong way, and flashbacks. As a result, the anxiety that comes with them does not reduce with time.

When you undergo PTSD treatment, it leads to proper memory processing, so that as time goes on, nightmares and flashbacks may subside and vanish entirely.

How Is Your Brain Affected by PTSD?

If you or someone you know is battling PTSD, you will need to learn how various parts of the brain work. This will enable you to have a thorough understanding of the condition and how to deal with the reactions that come with it—PTSD affects the way the brain functions.

Your brain is equipped with a system that aids in ensuring you survive in the face of danger. However, when you have PTSD, this system starts to malfunction and gets triggered with ease. When this happens, the parts of your brain that have to do with memory and thinking stop working entirely. The result of this is the difficulty in separating dangerous things happening now from those that occurred previously.

Scientific means of neuroimaging have allowed scientists to observe that PTSD results in unique biological changes in your brain. Although not every individual who experiences PTSD has the same symptoms or changes to the brain, there are patterns that we can understand and treat.

Various Areas of the Brain Affected By PTSD

The Amygdala

This is the part of your brain that is responsible for triggering your natural alarm system. When you encounter an uncomfortable or traumatic event, your amygdala sends a signal that triggers a fear response. This helps to keep you safe under the right circumstance, like if you are facing actual danger.

However, individuals with PTSD tend to have an excessive response. Imagine your home security alarms constantly going off, even when no one is breaking in. Annoying, right?

Your amygdala is the primitive part of your brain, designed to ensure that you survive. But when it doesn't work the way it should, it becomes very difficult to think rationally.

The Prefrontal Cortex (PFC)

This part of your brain helps you to think through your choices, observe your thought patterns, and stop when you realize that something you were initially scared of is not scary at all.

The prefrontal cortex aids in regulating emotional responses that the amygdala creates. In veterans with PTSD, the prefrontal cortex fails to do what it is meant to when required.

Other key functions of this part of the brain include:

- Triggering conscious actions
- Regulating attention and emotions
- Making decisions
- Understanding emotions

The PFC consists of various parts:

- **The ventromedial PFC:** This aids in suppressing negative emotions. It also helps in social and personal decision-making. What's more, it regulates extinction and plays a huge role in the latter aspects of memory consolidation.
- **The orbitofrontal cortex:** This is the area of the brain with the least information. It has a hand in sensory integration and signals unexpected punishments or rewards in specific situations. It also controls decision-making and emotions.
- **The dorsolateral PFC:** This is responsible for controlling the working memory and decision-making. The working memory stores transitory data before it is moved to long-term memory during the process of memory consolidation.

Overall, the PFC is linked to numerous brain functions, including controlling slow-wave sleep, also called deep sleep. It also helps with memory consolidation.

The Mid-Anterior Cingulate Cortex

This area of the brain has the role of monitoring conflict. In addition, it does the following:

- Processing physical pain
- Awareness of emotions
- Modifying autonomic functions like blood pressure and heart rate

The Hippocampus

This helps in regulating memory, spatial coding, and smell. Also, it helps with the storage of long-term memories by determining what is transferred from short-term to long-term memory. This process is what is known as memory consolidation. When the hippocampus is damaged, it can result in the release of excess cortisol, which is a stress hormone.

The Right Inferior Frontal Gyrus

This part of the brain has to do with controlling risk aversion. According to studies, transcranial magnetic stimulation of the right inferior frontal gyrus may minimize some risky behaviors.

Putting It All Together

An overactive amygdala alongside an underactive prefrontal cortex can result in a disastrous effect—similar to accelerating a power bike even when it isn't necessary, only to realize that the brakes are bad and you can't stop.

This can aid you in understanding why an individual dealing with PTSD may:

- Struggle with anxiety around things that seem similar to the trauma that resulted in PTSD
- Be triggered physically by events that should not result in a fear reaction
- Stay away from instances that may result in those intense reactions and emotions

How Does the Brain Respond to Trauma?

As discussed, your amygdala has the role of initiating the fight-or-flight response anytime it notices potential danger. It is a form of alarm system that steers you away from anything it feels is a threat.

Also, the amygdala interacts with other parts of the brain like the hippocampus, which releases the stress hormone cortisol. Then, the prefrontal cortex evaluates the reason for the response and decides if the body should remain on alert to handle the danger or if the brain can go ahead and calm the body down.

The prefrontal cortex aids in returning your body to normalcy when you find out that the threat may not be a danger to you or once the danger has passed.

When individuals suffer PTSD symptoms, the medial prefrontal cortex becomes hypoactive while the amygdala becomes hyperactive. In essence, the area of the brain responsible for triggering a fight-or-flight response reacts too powerfully, usually in a manner that does not align with the possible danger that comes with the threat.

In addition, the part of the brain tasked with the role of calming down this response does not function as it should.

The Consequences of Trauma

When you look at the functions of the numerous brain structures, you start to better understand how some PTSD symptoms can alter these brain structures.

Hypervigilance

As the amygdala overreacts, there is a release of norepinephrine, which the prefrontal cortex does not properly control or handle.

This results in individuals with PTSD experiencing hypervigilance symptoms. They are on high alert, which can make it difficult for them to stay calm and sleep.

An individual may feel that they are always nervous, and even the slightest triggers can make them feel as though they are dealing with their initial trauma once more.

Inaccurate Recall

Many PTSD symptoms may result in more trauma, especially due to hypersensitivity. There is evidence that all of these have to do with the hippocampus. This part of your brain is similar to the memory on your computer that stores files on its hard drive.

Typically, your hippocampus does everything possible to correctly remember an event and process it. However, because trauma causes a lot of pain and is a lot to take in, it is unable to code all of the information properly. This means you may spend time thinking about what occurred or remembering the vital details of the trauma.

Also, during fear conditioning, the hippocampus helps in encoding context. The moment the hippocampus does not function the way it should, it can affect the way an individual recalls a memory and remembers information. This is particularly prominent when it comes to memories that include an element of fear, like those related to trauma.

As regards PTSD symptoms, this leads to:

- Repeated memories that have to do with the event
- Dissociative flashbacks
- Distorted negative beliefs

Impulsive Behavior

A change to the right inferior frontal gyrus helps in explaining why individuals with PTSD may start to suddenly partake in extremely risky actions.

According to research, reduced cortical thickness in specific parts of the brain that have to do with response inhibition and emotional regulation, along with the right frontal gyrus, is associated with problems of impulse control in PTSD.

Wrap Up

Your prefrontal cortex, amygdala, and hippocampus all have a role to play with the actions and feelings that have to do with clear thinking, decision-making, fear, and memory.

Understanding the way they function can provide you with more clarity as to why some therapies can help you overcome PTSD.

Chapter 2:

PTSD and Your Loved

Ones

PTSD has a profound effect on your relationships. Dealing with these symptoms can be tough for both of the partners involved. And if it is someone you genuinely love, walking away would be the last thing on your mind.

PTSD can destroy connections because soon, the intimacy, kindness, and trust in the relationship dwindle—usually because the survivor stops showing all of these. In most cases, this reaction is due to the nightmares, flashbacks, isolation, and other symptoms the survivor starts to experience. Coupled with this, the survivor may feel intense shame and guilt.

While PTSD can destroy relationships, you can make sure it does not destroy yours. Many relationships end because the other partner does not recognize what the survivor is going through. However, if you properly arm yourself with the knowledge of how this condition can affect your relationship, then you can find the information you will require to build the relationship once more.

This is not impossible, but the first step is to understand what you are dealing with. Knowing this, let us look into some of the ways the symptoms that come with this condition can affect your loved one and your relationship.

How PTSD Impacts Your Relationship

General Numbness

PTSD numbs the survivor of the trauma. This is a defense mechanism, but the problem is that it becomes a permanent part of their lives. PTSD can result in the trauma survivor becoming disinterested in any social activity. They may even start to avoid things they used to love doing. Soon, they may seem distant and disconnected from everything around them, and this will include their partner.

This could lead to the partner feeling alienated and frustrated. Even when the partner tries to engage and reach out, they usually make no headway, and the partner may feel discouraged and disappointed. When this happens, the partner may start to become distant, too, since the survivor fails to reach out or respond. With time, this distance may grow wider, and could result in the end of the relationship.

Absence of Physical Intimacy

PTSD can be detrimental to trust. This is particularly prominent in victims of traumatic events like rape and other forms of physical violence—physical intimacy can be difficult and even non-existent. Reliving this type of trauma can lead to the survivor continually experiencing feelings of pain, abuse, and fear. All of these can make physical intimacy uncomfortable for them, and as a result, they tend to avoid it.

This disinterest in physical intimacy and other sexual activities can be surprising for the survivor, and could enhance their feelings of guilt or shame due to their inability to satisfy or show interest in their partners. Meanwhile, the partners of these individuals may feel unloved, lonely, and rejected when their sexual advances are constantly turned down.

Inconsiderate Demands, Irritation, and Control

A common symptom of trauma survivors is that they are always on edge. Due to their experience, they have no trust for anyone or anything in the world. This is especially prevalent in people who've experienced trauma like a violent assault, combat, or rape.

Let's use this story of John to further illustrate this point:

Heading home one night, John was walking down a dark alley. He had done this many times, so he was walking without a care in the world, and didn't notice the muggers hidden in the corner until it was too late. The first one knocked him down and tried to grab his bag, but John resisted, which infuriated the muggers more.

They started to rain blows on his head, and he was stabbed twice. The last thing he remembered was him thinking he was going to die before he passed out. He later woke up in the hospital, and according to the doctors, had suffered a severe concussion and a few broken bones. He was passed out for three days after the attack.

Ever since then, John always felt on edge. He had constant flashbacks of being jumped and never passed through any dark alleys alone anymore. However, this jumpiness extended to his home, too. The slightest sounds made him jumpy. Soon, he bought a gun that he kept underneath his pillow and was always on guard, ready to pull out his weapon at any time.

His wife and kids suffered, too, as John pulled his gun on them more than once, thinking it was someone trying to attack him. She also experienced interrupted sleep whenever he had a nightmare and jumped out of bed. The house became tense as his edginess was scary for his kids and his wife. There were also times when he snapped or acted out in anger when he discovered that the noise he was reacting to was just because of his kids.

This went on for a long time until his wife was forced to move to her parents' home with the kids and refused to come back until he got treatment.

This is a typical example of how PTSD can affect a person and their relationships. They could react to their loved ones with rage, unreasonable demands, and irritability. All of these can start to affect the partner if experienced constantly.

Soon, they may begin to feel pressure, fear, and resentment in the relationship and have no option but to leave. The survivor, on the other hand, also experiences shame and guilt because of how their new behavior is affecting the relationship.

Problems Sleeping

Many people who have PTSD suffer from disrupted sleep, insomnia, and nightmares. On top of this, the absence of sleep has been proven to worsen the symptoms of PTSD.

First, this means it may become impossible for partners to sleep together. If the PTSD survivor has insomnia, they won't be able to sleep, anyway. As well, nightmares may result in them jumping up in terror at odd hours of the night, which will be disruptive for the partner.

Soon, sleeping apart may further create a rift in intimacy. All of these may lead to both partners feeling tired and unable to handle stress. The person living with PTSD may feel frustrated and irritated at their inability to sleep because of the nightmares. Even if they have the urge to sleep, they try to fight it because they are avoiding nightmares. In the end, this leads to even more frustrations, which are then passed down to their partners.

Communication Problems

Communication is a vital part of every relationship, and if it is not prioritized, it can be problematic for all the parties involved. In fact, without proper communication, the relationship is as good as over.

PTSD may cause conversations to be brief and simple, and sometimes even non-existent. This can be very frustrating for the partner who is unable to communicate their feelings to the person with PTSD.

Critical Statements

People with PTSD often face symptoms like impulse control, rage, and anger. To deal with these troublesome emotions and urges, they may keep their feelings hidden and try to push others away through bad behavior. Another way they may protect themselves is through verbal abuse, to make their partners feel they are not happy or satisfied.

Partners may begin to feel isolated due to all of the toxic behavior and may also react by lashing out. Sometimes, this could escalate into physical altercations, which may put both partners at risk.

Over-Dependence

Some individuals who have PTSD tend to feel closed down by trauma. They don't trust themselves to trust the right people or to even function properly with the world. They have lost confidence in themselves and everything they stand for. This causes varied reactions in survivors. For some, the solution is to push their loved ones away, as we discussed above.

However, some of them may find themselves depending on their loved ones for everything. As a result, they may unknowingly drain the emotional resources of the partner, trying to offer support. This dependence may result in partners in feeling stressed and frustrated that they are unable to help.

Sometimes, the partners may find it difficult to cope even while doing everything they can.

Unhealthy Coping Methods

One unhealthy method of coping individuals with PTSD often turn to is alcohol and other substances. However, these provide only a temporary release and usually lead to addiction. What's more, these unhealthy coping mechanisms only make the PTSD symptoms even worse.

In a situation like this, the partner may be unable to handle the addiction, along with the other destructive symptoms that may arise. In worst cases, partners may find themselves moving toward unhealthy coping habits of their own, while others may find everything too much to handle and leave the relationship entirely.

In an intimate relationship, we are vulnerable because we expose our inner fears and desires. When suffering from PTSD, this vulnerability triggers other symptoms, which is usually evident to the person in a relationship with these individuals. Many of them can tell something is wrong, but since the person living with PTSD finds it hard to communicate and let others reach them, the real reason never comes out.

This may cause a relationship to become difficult and sometimes unbearable. In essence, if PTSD is not treated, it can result in sufferers neglecting loved ones and sometimes ending the relationship prematurely and in a very terrible way.

How Do People With PTSD
Experience Triggers?

Triggers are often linked to the five senses of sight, smell, taste, touch, and sound. They can come at any time and affect your loved one in a variety of ways. Below are some of the major symptoms experienced during a trigger.

I will be using examples shared with me by my sister, Susie, as well as Paul and Joan, two other people who have given me permission to share some of their experiences.

Flashbacks

For anyone with PTSD, a flashback is an experience that makes them relive the trauma they endured. A flashback is also a dissociative experience, meaning you will lose touch of the things happening around you for a brief period. It feels like you have been pulled out of your body, and into the time when the trauma occurred.

This flashback can also trigger a panic mode in the brain where the traumatic memory is stored, making the individual feel they are experiencing their trauma once more. To help you better understand how this works, think back to a time when you were driving and suddenly realize you have no recollection of how you moved from point A to B.

A flashback trigger is anything that acts as a reminder of your traumatic event. These can include a specific song, a sound, or a particular location. For many veterans, hearing fireworks can trigger flashbacks of their time on the frontlines.

The best way to describe how a flashback affects you is to imagine that your body keeps moving forward in time while your mind remains trapped in the past, continually reliving the trauma. When experiencing flashbacks, all your senses remain active.

You experience the same pressure, pain, and emotions, such as distress, horror, and fear you felt during the original incident. Other physical sensations include increased heart rates and trouble breathing.

Susie: I liken my flashbacks to the gates of hell.

[Do you know the gates of hell? These places are considered entryways to the underworld.]

I find myself moving to different locations, but as soon as I come across a trigger, I am dragged back to the same moment in the past—the moment where I experienced the traumatic event.

Hypervigilance

Hypervigilance is a state in which you are always on high alert. It involves high sensitivity to minor changes in your surroundings. This is a common symptom of people with PTSD, which they develop in a bid to protect themselves from future danger.

The dangers you're looking out for in this case are both real and assumed. You will find yourself constantly checking your surroundings for anything that may pose a threat, as well as any possible means of escape. Due to this symptom, you will often find yourself overreacting to minor things.

There are different situations that may trigger this kind of response. For most people, any sudden movement or noise can be startling. Others may avoid public gatherings, sit close to a wall to prevent anyone from sneaking up on them, or be close to the exit for a quick escape.

Paul: Hypervigilance is one thing I find very hard to explain. When I walk through the streets or even the hallways in my home, I feel there is something dangerous drawing close to me.

At this point, I'm always on guard, and I get startled by leaves falling on the ground. I guess this is better than the days when I hear someone whispering my name or footsteps approaching while I wait quietly in my closet.

Nightmares

For people with PTSD, it is usually challenging to differentiate nightmares from reality. This is because these nightmares play out exactly how the traumatic event occurred. As a result, they often find it difficult to fall asleep due to fear.

Everyone understands that nightmares are just scary dreams. This is why many people don't see this as a big deal. To know how nightmares affect people with PTSD, imagine being sure you went to bed and then finding yourself standing up, unable to determine if you're still asleep or awake.

Why is this so? It is because the nightmares are realistic. You can feel the physical pain and experience all the sensations that the event triggers. While you're still trying to figure out what's going on, you feel a tap on your shoulder or hear a knock on the door, and you're suddenly screaming in fear without knowing what happens next.

Joan: My nightmares always take me back to the scene of my trauma, and I feel like I'm experiencing it again for the first time. If I'm lucky, I wake up in time to escape the event, but it's always there waiting to continue the next time I fall asleep.

I feel like Nicolas Cage in the movie Next. *The only difference is that I can only relive one specific event over and over without being able to change it.*

Panic Attacks

A panic attack is a situation in which you experience extreme fear, along with various physical sensations, such as:

- Shaking
- Difficulty breathing
- Dizziness
- Heart palpitations
- Tingling hands
- Sweating

Panic attacks are frequent among those who have PTSD. When the attack occurs, you become unable to accept reality. Sometimes, you may also feel like you're losing control of yourself, and this scares you.

These panic attacks can affect your daily life, and there are usually no triggers. They often occur suddenly, without warning.

Susie: I hate my panic attacks. When they occur, I feel like I'm in The Shining, *scared of the next time Jack will appear. That is how my life is every day. I am always on edge.*

Sample Exercise

To gain a better understanding of how your loved ones feel, this exercise can help. The first thing you need to do is to try recalling an event from your past—an event after which you experienced anger, sadness, anxiety, and other negative feelings for an extended period.

When you recall the event, write it down in detail. The details of the event are crucial in boosting the effectiveness of this exercise. After writing this out, use these questions as a guide to help you draw out how you feel about it:

- Do you try to avoid any activity, conversation, place, or person you can associate with this event?
- Do you often have difficulties when trying to recall this event?
- Do you blame yourself for what happened?
- Does this event affect your sleep or concentration?
- Are there times when you have flashbacks about this event?
- Do you avoid memories of this event?
- Do you have negative self-thoughts like "It's my fault," "I can't trust anyone," or "I am a bad person"?

- Do you experience constant feelings of fear, shame, horror, or anger?
- Have you found it challenging to be truly happy or satisfied with life?

These are just a few questions that can put you on the same train of thought as your loved one. If you answer "yes" to a few of these questions, then you will have a little understanding of how they feel. In their case, they likely respond yes to all these questions.

Chapter 3:

Getting Help for Your

Loved One

Dealing with PTSD is difficult for every individual. You will also feel the burden of this disorder if you have a loved one dealing with it. To ease this burden, it's crucial to find a way to treat this disorder. Like with most other medical conditions, there are many treatment therapies and medications that can help with PTSD.

A common form of treatment is through psychotherapy. Some of the objectives of psychotherapy that make it a suitable alternative to drugs include the following:

- Helping you change how you think about the world, yourself, and other individuals.
- Dealing with other issues like depression, drug or alcohol abuse, and anxiety that relates to trauma.
- Helping you develop skills for the identification of your PTSD symptoms.

- Teaching you how to use your skills to deal with PTSD symptoms outside therapy.

To help yourself or a loved one overcome PTSD, you must be knowledgeable about the treatments available. In this chapter, you will learn about these treatments as well as their pros and cons.

Cognitive Processing Therapy

In dealing with PTSD, there is a need to address the thinking patterns of the patient. This is achievable through cognitive processing therapy (CPT). This therapy focuses on addressing the beliefs that lead to PTSD in an individual.

These include the pre-trauma beliefs and post-trauma beliefs. The conflict between these beliefs is the reason for PTSD.

Cognitive processing therapy addresses four areas.

- **The Symptoms**: The first step toward treatment using this therapy is to become more knowledgeable about your PTSD symptoms and the merits of undergoing treatment.
- **Skills**: The therapy helps in developing new skills that you can use in analyzing your feelings and thoughts. As a result, you begin to question,

challenge, and choose alternative ways to think about or respond to your trauma.

- **Your Beliefs**: Attaining an equilibrium between your view of the world pre-trauma and post-trauma is crucial. For most individuals with PTSD, there is often a change in their opinion about the world after the traumatic experience.
- **Feelings and Thoughts**: An increase in awareness is another crucial part of this therapy. This will help you understand how your current beliefs cause pain and prevent you from moving forward.

Like many other treatments, CPT usually occurs in sessions that can last up to 60 minutes. The procedure is often spread over twelve sessions with one session each week or biweekly.

How Does It Work?

The use of CPT in treating PTSD begins with psychoeducation. Psychoeducation is a term that describes the process of informing or educating individuals who are currently receiving or intending to receive mental health services. In this case, the information you receive focuses on your emotions, thoughts, and PTSD.

Through psychoeducation, you gain more clarity on how your emotions and thoughts relate, and their effect on PTSD. This will help in identifying some recurring thoughts that help promote the symptoms of PTSD.

After the process of psychoeducation, you must show your understanding of the effect of the traumatic event on your world, the people around you, and yourself. This is written in an impact statement.

Now, you can start assessing your trauma. This involves writing a detailed account of your worst traumatic event. To deal with the issue of avoidance, you will read this account out loud in the next session. This helps you feel the emotions associated with the event.

Self-blaming thoughts and other unhelpful thoughts are addressed at this point. To do this, the therapist will use various strategies, including Socratic questioning. Any maladaptive thinking you have will undergo a corrective modification.

The entire therapy focuses on helping you develop the skills you need to identify and address unhelpful thinking. You will continuously assess your beliefs regarding the traumatic event and modify them accordingly. The goal of this process is to ensure you can utilize the skills you develop outside of therapy.

This will help improve your quality of life and overall day-to-day functioning. There are certain areas that a therapist may focus on, such as:

- Control
- Safety
- Intimacy
- Trust
- Esteem
- Power

The reason for this is that your traumatic experiences usually have the most effect on these areas. In some cases, the therapist may decide to focus on the use of cognitive techniques rather than the written method of trauma accounting. You can also choose to have the CPT in structured group sessions, or as an individual.

One practical action that most therapists take is to give patients out-of-session assignments. This makes it easier to understand the technique.

Benefits of This Treatment

You Can Combine It With Medication

Most medical conditions usually require medications for treatment. But what happens when medication alone doesn't work? It is in such situations that cognitive processing therapy has proven to be useful.

Since factors such as the environment have a significant influence on our thoughts, medications alone won't be enough to overcome PTSD.

Age Isn't a Limiting Factor

Several treatments become less effective, depending on the age of the patient, but this isn't the case with CPT. It remains effective regardless of the patient's age.

Disadvantages of This Treatment

- It takes a lot of time to complete the treatment.
- It is less effective for individuals who have a more severe case of PTSD.
- Therapy requires effort from both the patient and the therapist to be effective.

Prolonged Exposure Therapy

Another trusted therapy that is available for treating PTSD is prolonged exposure therapy, or PET. It is approved for use by the Department of Veterans Affairs and Defense, and the American Psychiatric Association.

Depression, painful thoughts, hypervigilance, hopelessness, and nightmares are some of the effects of PTSD on individuals. The simplest way many people know how to overcome these effects is through avoidance.

However, by confronting the situations, memories, and feelings that promote trauma-related fears, an individual can overcome PTSD. This is the simple idea behind prolonged exposure therapy. An individual who undergoes this therapy will have the opportunity to learn that there is no real danger in these cues, memories, or situations.

To make it easy for an individual to transition into the therapy, it is often spread over three months. This is further subdivided into eight to 15 sessions, with each session lasting an hour or two. Differences between the length of each session depend on the time required for the individual to gain adequate exposure.

There are a few unique types of exposures that therapists use during the treatment.

- **Imaginal Exposure:** During imaginal exposure, you will visualize yourself experiencing the traumatic event. This visualization must be in detail so you can induce the feelings that cause fear and deal with them. This form of exposure is used for more uncommon fears or unique events that are difficult to replicate.
- **In Vivo Exposure:** If the traumatic event can be traced to a specific location, then in vivo exposure is required. This may be in your office, riding on a bus, or flying on a plane. The therapy will occur in the location that induces the trauma.

- **Virtual Reality Exposure:** Virtual reality is becoming more relevant in the treatment of various conditions. For PTSD, you can trigger the stimuli of traumatic events through sights and sounds generated on a computer. Virtual reality exposure can be in a CAVE environment, on a computer display, or through the use of a VR headset. The CAVE environment is a compartment in the shape of a cube that consists of audio equipment and projectors for virtual reality.
- **Interoceptive Exposure:** This form of exposure focuses on inducing the stimuli that cause your trauma. You don't need to be exposed to the trauma in this case. If the stimulus is a difficulty in breathing, then you may perform exercises or workouts to induce this physical sensation. Repeated exposure to this stimulus changes how you react to it if it occurs due to trauma.

How Does It Work?

In using exposure therapy to deal with PTSD, there are a few things you must understand. These help in explaining the effectiveness of the therapy.

Habituation

This explains the weakening of your response to stimuli after continuous exposure. It implies that by continuously exposing you to your trauma, PET can help you get familiar with it until you no longer fear it.

Emotional Processing

Exposure helps you understand both your fears and your emotions, helping you become more comfortable dealing with anxiety and fears when they appear in moderation.

Extinction

The reason for your reaction to traumatic events is due to association. You learn to associate these events or fears to a specific physical response. Exposure therapy helps to erase the association you have created.

The absence of this association eliminates the need for any extreme response when you experience these situations.

Benefits of This Treatment

Minimizes Environmental Sensitivity

Numerous environmental cues trigger PTSD. Learning to overcome the suffering these cues can cause is one of the significant benefits of exposure therapy.

Repeated exposure to these cues assists the patient in understanding that these cues are not dangerous.

Knowing How to Live With Fear

Various situations can induce fear, and prolonged exposure therapy helps patients learn how to live with these fears. You understand fear to be a part of nature, and therefore avoid being paralyzed from it.

It Helps Control Anxiety

Since you face the stimuli over and over, you become less sensitive to it, which in turn minimizes anxiety.

Increases Social Skills

Anxiety usually prevents individuals from communicating with others or providing input in conversations. Prolonged exposure therapy helps you learn to relax in social situations.

Eliminates Obsessive-Compulsive Behaviors

In dealing with fear and anxiety, many individuals develop obsessive-compulsive behaviors, which may be in the form of actions they must perform before heading out for the day. Exposure therapy helps overcome the need for these behaviors.

Disadvantages of This Treatment

Patients will be exposed to situations that cause severe pain, anxiety, or trauma. Doing this can do more harm to some patients. This is often the case if the psychotherapist doesn't have sufficient training on administering this form of therapy.

Eye Movement Desensitization and Reprocessing (EMDR)

This is another psychotherapy technique that is useful in overcoming PTSD, trauma, and psychological stress. During the therapy, the therapist is responsible for coordinating your eye movement.

While recalling the traumatic events, the eye movement serves as a form of distraction. This distraction is necessary to lessen the emotional effect the traumatic memories have on you. Also, patients are exposed to the experiences for only short periods to minimize any impact.

Taking these steps, your psychological responses to traumatic thoughts and memories become weaker than usual. Repeating the therapy over a long period will help minimize the effects of the traumatic memories.

How Does It Work?

EDMR therapy consists of eight phases. To complete these phases, the treatment usually requires up to 12 sessions. Here is a look at the various phases:

- **Phase 1:** This phase deals with your treatment planning and history. It is an evaluation of your past to help determine the right path to take with your treatment. Topics you will discuss will include the memories you want to treat and your trauma.

- **Phase 2:** This is the preparation phase, and it exposes you to several coping strategies. These include psychological and emotional stress management techniques like mindfulness and deep breathing.

- **Phase 3:** This is the assessment phase, during which the therapist engages in memory identification. By identifying these memories, they become the targets of the therapy along with any component associated with them, such as the physical sensations they trigger.

- **Phases 4 through 7:** These are the treatment phases. Starting in phase 4, you will start undergoing treatment through various EMDR techniques. You will need to concentrate on any negative image or thoughts relating to the targeted memory. You will also make specific eye movements concurrently, and the therapist will guide you through these movements. This is a bilateral simulation.

Some situations require the inclusion of other movements to boost the effectiveness of the therapy. The therapist then ends the simulation and asks you to identify the various feelings and thoughts you're currently experiencing. You may find yourself feeling distressed during the simulation.

The therapist will get you back to the present day as soon as you show signs of distress. As you repeat the therapy, this distress begins to disappear.

- **Phase 8:** This is the evaluation phase, and also the final phase of the therapy. Both you and the therapist perform the evaluation. How much progress have you made? This is the question you must answer.

Benefits of This Treatment

There are some significant benefits of EMDR therapy. These include the following:

Trauma Identification

Most traumatic memories are so painful you don't want to recall them. As a result, you end up blocking them out. EMDR helps you accept these traumatic memories to make way for true healing.

No Negative Side Effects

If you're worried about the side effects of adopting this therapy, then you will be happy to know there are none.

Improvements Occur Rapidly

A considerable benefit of EDMR is the possibility of noticing positive changes after a single session. This feeling of progress motivates you as a patient to continue with the therapy.

Identifying Stressors and Reactions

In dealing with traumatic memories, many individuals choose to react to the effects by taking drugs or alcohol. The EMDR therapy helps you deal with the cause, rather than responding to the effect.

Disadvantages of This Treatment

One issue many people have with EMDR is due to its short history. This history begins in 1989, which means there is no long-term study to prove its effectiveness.

Stress Inoculation Training

In the treatment of PTSD, another common form of cognitive-behavioral therapy (CBT) in use is the stress inoculation training (SIT). This training is an effective way to ensure your body can quickly put up its defenses anytime it is exposed to cues, reminders, and triggers of PTSD-related anxiety and fear. It has an effect that is similar to the use of a vaccine against certain diseases.

SIT promotes these responses by focusing on improving your confidence. This is possible through exposure to lower levels of stress. A session in SIT can be for 20 minutes or extended to last for a full hour.

The training is spread over eight to 15 sessions, which are completed within three months or a year.

How Does It Work?

There are several things a patient can learn during the stress inoculation training. These include an improved awareness and identification of various cues and triggers that promote anxiety and fear.

In dealing with fear and anxiety, specific coping skills are crucial. These include:

Deep Breathing

The first coping technique to identify is the deep breathing from your diaphragm. The initial step is to learn the correct form of deep breathing, and then to make it a habit through practice. You can engage in your practice during the intervals between each session.

Muscle Relaxation Training

This training teaches you the right way to tense and release your muscles. You will repeat this on the major muscle groups in the body to aid in relaxation.

Role-Playing

Role-playing is a means through which you can utilize each coping technique in simulations of the real events. In this case, you will be simulating a stress-inducing situation. To overcome this, you must use the coping strategies you have learned.

A therapist is usually responsible for setting up the events of the role-play.

Addressing Negative Behaviors and Thoughts

How you handle your negative thoughts and behaviors is crucial in dealing with PTSD. A part of SIT aids you in learning the right actions to take in an anxiety-provoking situation. To do this, you must be able to identify various cues related to your trauma while maintaining control of multiple aspects of the situation, including how you react.

The Silent Self-Talk

For many individuals, silent self-talk is a part of their life. If you don't already do this, then this is the right time to start. However, silent self-talk in this situation will differ a bit from what you're used to doing.

Here, the goal of your self-talk is to encourage yourself and make positive statements to yourself anytime you begin to notice any form of demeaning or negative thoughts.

The skills you learn during this training are easy to apply in your life. It is common to have a recording of each training session to assist you in practicing each coping strategy. Ensure you learn how to identify negative thoughts, cues, and triggers to help you deal with them quickly.

Stages of Stress Inoculation Training

There are three stages of SIT that you must understand.

Conceptualization Stage

During the conceptualization stage, you receive lots of information on stress and various stress reactions. Other things you learn include the effects of bad coping strategies, cognitive distortion, appraisal, and other vital concepts.

Skills Acquisitions and Rehearsal

Your needs as the patient determine the skills you learn during this stage. Using your strengths and weaknesses as a guide, the therapist will select the most crucial skills for the process. These usually include a combination of these skills:

- Relaxation
- Socialization
- Problem-solving
- Emotion regulation
- Communication
- Cognitive appraisal

Application and Follow Through

In this stage, you have the opportunity to practice the various skills you have learned. You can engage in a simulation of events using various methods such as modeling and vicarious learning, role-playing, and visualization exercises.

Benefits of This Treatment

There are several benefits of SIT.

- In contrast to the use of drugs, there is no risk of addiction, withdrawal symptoms, or other side effects.

- It has a long-lasting effect since it deals with the root cause of stress in eliminating the symptoms.

Disadvantages of This Treatment

The main downside with the use of SIT is the necessary money and time investment. Since it requires several months to be effective, the treatment is usually more expensive than drugs.

Medication

In treating PTSD, there are several useful medications available. The classifications of these medications include:

Antidepressants

For those dealing with concentration and sleep problems due to PTSD, antidepressants can be of immense benefit. Of the numerous antidepressants available, only selective serotonin reuptake inhibitor (SSRI) medications have specific approval for PTSD treatment by the Food and Drug Administration (FDA). Examples include sertraline and paroxetine.

Antipsychotics

Drugs that fall into this category include prazosin and risperidone. In treating PTSD, there have been a few studies indicating the effectiveness of prazosin in minimizing nightmares. Regardless of the potential benefits, getting advice from a doctor is crucial.

Anti-Anxiety Medications

Doctors usually recommend these drugs for only a short period, despite their effectiveness in dealing with anxiety. This is due to the risk of abuse of anti-anxiety medications.

Other medications are used in the treatment of PTSD, such as:

- Atypical antidepressants such as venlafaxine and mirtazapine
- Mood stabilizers such as lithium and carbamazepine
- Monoamine oxidase inhibitors like phenelzine and isocarboxazid

Certain drugs can be addictive, which you will learn about in a different section. In prescribing medications for treating PTSD, a doctor will need to determine the right combination and doses of the medication.

Medications in the treatment of PTSD will be prescribed if any of the following is true:

- The traumatic event is likely to continue occurring in the future, making any form of psychological treatment irrelevant or ineffective. This is the case with individuals experiencing domestic violence.
- You opt-out of all forms of psychological treatment.
- The presence of other medical conditions that diminish the effectiveness of psychological treatment. Depression can be one of these conditions.
- After undergoing psychological treatment, there is no significant benefit.

Medications such as phenelzine and amitriptyline are only available for use in the presence of a mental health specialist that acts as a supervisor.

Individuals who don't notice a significant improvement in their condition when using medications usually have their dosage adjusted. For those who experience improvement, it is common to be on these medications for up to 12 months. After this period, withdrawal of the medications commences, and this can last for four weeks or more.

There is usually a possible side effect and withdrawal symptoms for most medications. These are part of the information you will get from your doctor. If the drug is withdrawn very slowly, withdrawal symptoms may be avoided.

Medication Abuse

A significant issue with using medications in treating PTSD is the possibility of patients abusing the drugs. Addiction is a common occurrence with anti-anxiety medications such as Xanax and Ativan.

Medication abuse occurs the moment you decide to make use of these drugs contrary to the recommendation of your doctor. For many individuals, medication abuse often happens when they try to overcome anxiety and panic symptoms by consuming beyond the recommended dose.

As a result, they need to rely on high doses of these drugs to deal with some situations. A clear indication of abuse is an overreliance on these drugs and a lack of control despite the apparent adverse effects on you.

Deciding the Best Option for a Loved One

There are many factors to consider when selecting the right option for treating PTSD in a loved one. At this point, it is crucial you consider the following:

Personal Traits of Your Loved One

There are different traits you must identify in your loved one. Their personality, likes, dislikes, and ease of learning all have a significant impact on the type of psychotherapy they will need.

This will also help in determining if an individual session or group session will be more effective. Their individual struggles will indicate whether they will need therapy, medication, or a combination of both.

When to Start

Choosing the right time for your loved one to begin therapy is vital. In making your decision, you must consider the availability of space. Is there an opening for new participants, or do you have to wait for a spot to open up?

This is often the case with group sessions. The therapist may also have a full schedule, which can hinder the plans you've made. It is important that you find this out and book an appointment early.

Looking for Psychotherapists Around You

What type of therapy is available in your location? Do you have any information on the therapists around? These are the essential questions you will need to answer.

You can start out by asking other individuals within the neighborhood. It's easy to get an honest opinion on a therapist from those that have worked with them previously. You can also source for information online.

The psychotherapist should be trustworthy and easy to connect with. This will help improve the effectiveness of the treatment.

Number of Weekly Sessions

Knowing how long you want to leave your loved one in therapy will help you determine the number of weekly sessions. Do you need one session per week? Or will three sessions be more effective?

Sample Exercise

Using all of the information above, try to determine the best option for your loved one.

To do this, determine their personality type and write it out. Next, think of how they learn, what they like and don't like, their specific characteristics, and what they respond to best.

After you have listed this out, study it, and determine the method that will be ideal for them. If you come up with more than one option, list them out and deliberate on the best choice.

Chapter 4:

Support Through Recovery

Recovery from PTSD can be extremely hard on both people in the relationship, because it is difficult to understand the actions of your loved one. You may feel like you have to exercise caution when around the person. And soon, it may seem like you are with someone completely different.

Additionally, you may take on a more substantial portion of the responsibilities in the home, while dealing with anger outbursts and all the other frustrating PTSD symptoms from your partner. This can cause you a huge level of discomfort, which makes it very easy for you to develop some resentment, too.

However, you need to note that when a person is dealing with PTSD, they may not always be in control of how they act. In most cases, these individuals are always alert, which makes them feel unsafe and vulnerable. This can result in depression, mistrust, irritability, and other PTSD symptoms that your loved ones don't know how to get rid of.

With the right support from the people around them, including you, they can get past the trauma and live life the way they should.

So, how can you provide support to a loved one who has experienced trauma?

Helping Someone With PTSD

Offer Social Support

When people have PTSD, one of the first things they commonly do is isolate themselves, withdrawing from family and friends. Under normal circumstances, boundaries are healthy for all individuals, and it is fine to respect them.

However, when it comes to someone who has PTSD, the support you offer can help them overcome most of the feelings that come with the condition. Experts are of the notion that face-to-face support from other individuals is crucial for recovering from PTSD.

It may be challenging to determine how best to show your support or love for someone with PTSD. You can't force someone to accept the help you are offering; neither can you force them to get better. However, you can be influential in their recovery process by spending some time with them.

To make this work, there are a few things you need to note:

- **Don't force your loved one to speak**. Trauma is not an easy or fun experience, and this is why it can be hard for individuals who have PTSD to talk about their experiences. For some, it can worsen the situation, which is why many individuals who suffer from trauma prefer to avoid speaking or even thinking about it.

  So, instead of forcing them to speak, gently let them know you are willing to hear them out anytime they want to talk, or spend time with them when they don't feel like speaking. To offer someone with PTSD comfort, you need to make them feel accepted and that they have someone to depend on.

- **Engage in normal activities with them**. Try to engage in activities that make your loved one forget about their trauma. These should be normal things that have no connection to the trauma they experienced.

  You could urge them to pursue hobbies they enjoy, engage in mindful exercises, or even spend time with friends. All of these would help them feel happier and get their mind off the trauma they experienced, all of which can be helpful in the recovery process.

- **Let your loved one decide**. Instead of telling your partner what to do, let them make decisions. PTSD does not affect everyone the same way; however, most individuals can tell what activities can help them relax and stay safe. Listen to your loved one and do what they want so you can offer them the best level of companionship and support.

- **Deal with your stress**. Don't forget yourself while caring for someone else. If you are not focused and calm, it will be difficult for you to offer your loved one the support they need for recovery. Keep your stress in check so you can better cater to your loved one.

- **Don't be in a rush.** Recovery is not a process that happens overnight. It will require time, and, in most cases, there are usually a few setbacks. Don't give up midway, and if any setback occurs, see it as a learning experience. Remain positive and continue to offer your loved one the support they require.

- **Increase your PTSD knowledge base**. The better educated you are about the condition and the various treatment options, symptoms, and so on, the better you will be at helping your loved one. If you know what to expect and how to deal with anything that arises, it will be easier to help out.

- **Expect all kinds of feelings.** Caring for someone with PTSD is hard, and it can be extremely frustrating. For this reason, you may experience various emotions, ranging from positive to negative. This is understandable, and even if you develop negative feelings, you need to keep your mind open and accept them. Developing these feelings does not imply you don't cherish your loved ones, but only means you are human.

Master the Art of Listening

As stated, many people living with PTSD find it difficult to speak about their experiences or what they are going through. However, when they are ready and decide to open up, you will need to show interest and listen without any judgment or expectation. Your goal should not be to provide a solution to their problem, but to show you care about their well-being. A good way to do this is to listen attentively.

It may be necessary for the person living with PTSD to speak about their trauma numerous times. This is to be expected and is part of the healing process. Expect this and listen attentively no matter how many times you have heard the story. If you lash out at them out of frustration, they may go back into their shell and never open up to you again.

Even if some of the things you hear are not easy to listen to, you need to respect their responses and feelings.

To help encourage good communication, there are a few things to avoid when trying to show your support:

- Don't stop your loved ones from saying what bothers them and the things they feel.
- Don't tell them what actions you feel they "should" take.
- Don't give empty answers when they open up.
- Don't accuse them of being the cause of all the problems you are dealing with in the relationship.
- Don't make them feel bad because they are not getting over the trauma as fast as you expect, or not coping as well as someone else.
- Don't make them feel as though their traumatic experience is irrelevant or invalid. Regardless of the opinions you may have concerning the matter, keep them to yourself.
- Don't make demands or give ultimatums. This never ends well.
- Don't interrupt them by speaking about your own feelings or personal experiences. It should be about them and how they feel if you are serious about helping them go through the situation.

Help Rebuild Safety and Trust

As we discussed, trauma makes a person feel vulnerable and lose faith in the world around them. Depending on the kind of trauma they're dealing with, they may start to see the world as a scary and dangerous place, which affects their trust in themselves and other people. You can contribute to the recovery of your loved one by helping them rebuild their feeling of security.

To do this, the following may be of help:

- **Build routines.** Having a consistent and predictable structure can help restore security and stability for individuals with PTSD. This is the case for both children and adults.

  Establishing routines could involve getting your loved one to join you for a run every morning, doing some housework, or maintaining a regular schedule regarding sleep, wake up, and mealtimes, as well as time where you both enjoy each other's company.

- **Show that you are there.** Let your loved one know that you are committed to the relationship and that you are available to offer them support and love regardless of how long it takes.

- **Reduce stress in the home.** Do all you can to make your home as stress-free as possible. Make certain that they have adequate time to relax and rest. Also, give them the space they need to get better.

- **Keep your promises.** You can rebuild trust by proving to your loved ones that they can depend on you. Whenever you make a promise, ensure that you are consistent and do whatever you said you would.

- **Make plans.** Making plans and talking about the future can help PTSD sufferers deal with the feeling that they have a limited future.

- **Highlight their strengths.** Let your loved ones know that you believe in them and their capacity to overcome the condition. Point out all of the positive qualities they have and the things they have achieved so far.

- **Inspire them to join a support group.** By interacting with others who have experienced similar traumatic events, they can feel less damaged and alone.

Prepare for Triggers and Manage Them

A trigger is any place, person, or situation that makes your loved one remember their trauma and causes PTSD symptoms like nightmares or flashbacks.

In some cases, triggers may be easy to identify. For example, a person who was sexually assaulted may be triggered by a movie depicting sexual assault. Other triggers may not be instantaneous and can be more difficult to determine, such as the weather. For instance, someone could be triggered by the rain if it was raining during their trauma.

Sometimes, triggers may also be internal, as certain sensations and feelings can result in PTSD symptoms.

Let us take a look at these in detail below.

External PTSD Triggers

- Sounds, smells, and sights linked with the trauma
- Nature—seasons, weather, and so on
- Relevant times or dates like birthdays and universes, or even precise moments of the day.
- Circumstances that feel limiting, like being in a crowd or being stranded in
- traffic.
- Medical facilities, hospitals, or burials
- Family, work, financial, or relationship issues
- Media coverage associated with trauma or conversations about negative events

Internal PTSD Triggers

- Any sensation in the body that lets one remember the trauma like scars, wounds, pain, or a similar injury.
- Powerful emotions like feelings of being trapped or helplessness
- Physical discomforts like thirst, hunger, sexual frustration, and illnesses
- Feelings toward members of the family, which can include mixed feelings of resentment, love, and vulnerability.

Learn What Triggers Them

Since everyone is affected differently by PTSD, it will be a good idea to learn all of your loved one's specific internal and external triggers. Having in-depth knowledge of these triggers will help you avoid them and be ready whenever a flashback occurs.

Develop a Plan for PTSD Triggers

Ask your loved ones how they dealt with triggers previously that seemed to help them stay calm, and those that did not. Next, you can develop a plan for how you will react when a trigger arises subsequently.

You can also plan with your loved one as to how you should react when they have a flashback or nightmare. With a plan in place, the situation can be less complicated for you both to handle. What's more, it will be easier to keep your loved one calm.

Helping a Loved One Who Is Experiencing a Flashback

A flashback is an intense experience where an individual relives parts of a traumatic event. If your loved one is experiencing a flashback, it can be tricky to know how to assist them.

However, you can help out if you have the right information.

- As gently as you can, let your loved one know they are only experiencing a flashback. Tell them that even though the feeling is real, the event is not repeating itself. This is important because flashbacks are vivid, and they may start to act like they are actually in the flashback.
- Help them remember their environment. You can ask them to tell you what they see around them and describe it out loud. By doing this, they can remember they are in a safe zone and that the flashback is not real.
- Avoid moving suddenly or in a manner that could frighten them. This is because of their constant feeling of being on edge could make them always feel as though they are in danger.

Additionally, you may want to avoid crowding the individual.

- Tell them to take slow, deep breaths, as hyperventilation can trigger an enhanced feeling of panic. Encouraging them to take these slow breaths can help them feel calm once more.
- Respect their personal space. Don't touch them without permission, as doing this could result in them feeling trapped, which could result in their feeling more violent and agitated.

Pay Attention to the Warning Signs

When trying to support your loved one, you may observe some changes in their behavior.

You might see a change in the behavior of the person you want to support. For example:

- Mood shifts, like becoming easily irritated, angry, or upset
- Change to energy levels, like lack of focus or extreme focus
- Changes in work performance, like missing deadlines or arriving late

If you observe these in an individual close to you, ask them how they feel. This may encourage them to let you in on what is going on.

Manage Anger and other Explosive Behavior

PTSD makes it difficult for people to manage their impulses and emotions. This may be evident as moodiness, explosive anger, and irritability in your loved ones.

People with PTSD deal with frequent emotional and physical stress. Also, since they are often unable to have an uninterrupted sleep, there is a huge chance that they are always tired and on edge, which increases the possibility of them overreacting to normal stressors.

For many individuals dealing with PTSD, anger may be an alternative to other feelings like helplessness and sadness. Instead of seeming vulnerable and weak, anger gives them the power they need while others try to push down their anger till it explodes unexpectedly.

Some ways to do this include:

- **Take note of anger warnings signs**. These could include clenched fists or jaws, as well as increasing voices. When this happens, do all you can to make sure the situation does not escalate.
- **Try to stay calm**. During an outburst from your loved one, do everything possible to remain calm. Becoming agitated yourself will only make the situation worse, but staying calm will let your loved one know that everything is

fine and will ensure the situation does not escalate.

- **Ask how you can make things better**. For instance, ask what you can do to help, or suggest a fun activity or change of environment.
- **Make safety a priority.** If your loved one only seems to get angrier even with all your efforts to calm them down, it's best to remove yourself from the situation. You can do this by leaving home for some time or locking yourself in another part of the home. If you are worried that your loved one may be a danger to themselves or others, it may be best to reach out to the authorities.

Care for Yourself

Prioritizing your loved one while abandoning your own needs is a bad idea and can result in secondary traumatization. After listening to stories of trauma or witnessing scary PTSD symptoms like nightmares and flashbacks, you are likely going to feel overwhelmed. The more overwhelmed you feel, the more you face the possibility of you becoming traumatized, too.

To ensure you have the capacity to help out your loved ones and that you don't suffer from secondary trauma, it's best to care for yourself at all times.

- **Get your support system**. Find a support group or depend on close friends, family members, or a therapist. It can be very beneficial to speak about what you are dealing with.

- **Take care of your physical needs**. Work out, eat right, get enough rest, and deal with any medical problems.

- **Don't give up your personal life**. Don't let go of your hobbies, friends, or things that make you happy. It is essential to have activities that you look forward to and enjoy.

- **Share the responsibility**. Reach out to other members of your family and friends for help so you can relax and rejuvenate.

- **Create healthy boundaries**. Be truthful about what you can offer. Understand your limits and let your loved one and other people involved know these limits, and make certain you follow through.

Speaking to People With PTSD

When your loved one lets you in on their condition, you have the chance to provide support through conversations.

However, many people tend to respond the wrong way, which can make matters more complicated. To ensure this does not happen with your loved one and push them back into their shell, you will need to learn the right way to respond when they reach out to you.

How to Respond

There are numerous positive ways to react if your loved one informs you that they have PTSD:

- **Ask questions.** How can I be of help to you? Are there moments when your symptoms worsen? What can I do during those periods? You can create similar open-ended questions to this when responding to your loved one.

- **Understand their plight.** Our responses have a lot of influence on the way PTSD sufferers feel. For instance, someone who experienced combat may not be okay with movies or games with loud gunshots and explosions. Before the trauma, they may have been fine with these things, but now, they may not be comfortable with it. Request their permission before you do a thing like this. Asking allows them to make a choice, so they are not taken unawares if you do decide to play.

- **Offer them a feeling of control.** Once a person has experienced trauma, they may feel like they have no control over their lives. This is why asking for permission and seeing if they want something can do a lot of good.

- **Exercise patience.** If your loved one seems to flake on plans or doesn't seem comfortable with the activities you used to do together previously, don't get angry or frustrated. Instead, ask them what they would prefer and if they would rather do something with fewer individuals.

- **Offer to lend a listening ear and helping hand.** The life of your loved one may not be the same anymore due to PTSD. They may not go to social functions any longer, or they might stop going to work. They may also avoid going out at night or taking public transportation entirely.

In cases like this, it may be helpful to offer them encouragement and let them know you're there if they need you. For example, request to go with them if they are worried about heading to a particular area. This will help them see that everything is going to be okay.

- **Do not judge.** Your loved one may feel shame or guilt as a result of their traumatic experience. This is usually the case with people who have PTSD. They may feel they were responsible for what happened to them or did something to deserve it. In this situation, the best thing you can do is to let them know you are there to listen without any form of judgment.

Don't Minimize

When your loved one with PTSD lets you know about their condition, respect it. Do not trivialize what they are going through—instead, validate their feelings.

Also, there are a few things you should not say:

- Don't ask why they're not feeling better yet.
- Don't tell them to look at the bright side. There is no bright side about having to constantly be on edge and deal with flashbacks.
- Don't compare their trauma to that of someone else. Everybody experiences trauma differently. Also, doing this makes them feel like their own trauma is less valid.
- Don't give unsolicited advice. This will make your loved one feel like you are trying to fix them. Instead, just let them know they have your support.
- Generally, you will want to avoid anything that makes them feel they should not be feeling the way they do. Besides, you should not force them to engage in activities they are not prepared for.

- Don't push your loved one to seek counseling when they are not in the right frame of mind. Also, don't force them to go to a location that reminds them of their trauma. Doing these could only worsen their condition, which is certainly not what you want.

Suggest Help

When your loved one is dealing with this condition, you may calmly and gently recommend that they get help. If you notice any of the warning signs, like they have started to withdraw and isolate themselves, or are avoiding places they used to love, or perhaps just don't seem as happy as they used to be anymore, you could say, "Do you think it would be helpful if you speak to someone? I can look for a great person if you want."

A professional who deals in trauma can help your loved one by making a diagnosis and discussing a treatment option, like one of the ones we discussed in the earlier chapter.

As you can see, support can be highly beneficial in ensuring your loved one gets the recovery they need.

Brief Exercise

Now, take a look back at how your loved one was acting when they exhibited PTSD symptoms, like flashbacks or nightmares. If there were other symptoms, feel free to write them down.

Reflect on how you handled the situation using the information we have covered so far. Did you handle it properly? Did it turn out positive?

If it did, good—keep doing what you're doing, and use the information to refine what you already know.

If it did not, what do you think you can do in the future to ensure the outcome is better? Write this down and remember to go through the information if the situation arises once more.

Chapter 5:

Communicating With Your Loved One

Communication skills are crucial if you want the best out of life. This is true of work and personal relationships, but the right communication skills can also help you improve your interactions with a person with PTSD.

Loved ones with PTSD usually deal with prolonged fear and stress. The traumatic events they keep replaying in their minds often affect how they interact with others and the world. For most, they usually have a comfort zone, which is often their home. Anywhere outside this zone is seen as a hostile environment. Despite being comfortable at home, they likely still experience difficulties coming out of their bubble. This is why they often find it hard to interact.

In addition to developing the right communication skills, you must also make the environment as comfortable as possible for your loved one with PTSD. The first step is to remove anything that can cause stress or could act as a trigger. When people with PTSD are under extreme stress, it affects their behavior and communication. There are several coping strategies that sufferers adopt, and you must learn the strategy that works best for your loved one.

Remaining supportive and calm is another crucial step in promoting communication. Staying calm will help your loved one feel safe. If the situation or environment becomes tense, then you can expect to notice more symptoms of PTSD. This is how they react to threats.

The last thing you need to remember is that you need to be patient and tolerant. Don't interrupt your loved ones when they are talking—give them enough room to express themselves as much as necessary. If they want to repeat the experience or story, let them do so to their heart's content. Talking about these events is a crucial part of the healing process. Being a good listener is more than just hearing what a person says.

You must be observant and take note of the non-verbal cues. This is how people convey most of their message. Posture, tone of voice, facial expression, body movement, physiological changes, and eye contact are all non-verbal cues you will need to pay attention to.

You can learn when the conversation is becoming uncomfortable for your loved one through these non-verbal cues. Emotional awareness is another aspect that can help with this. Emotions have a significant impact on communication with a person dealing with PTSD.

Take note of both the positive and negative emotions experienced during the conversation. Exhibiting emotional awareness through empathy will promote effective communication. Now that you understand the basics, you can focus on improving your communication skills.

Adverse Effects of PTSD on Communication Skills

Flashbacks, nightmares, depression, and anxiety are just a few of the harmful effects of PTSD. Another area where the impact of this disorder is noticeable is in an individual's communication skills. There are several ways through which PTSD may mess with your ability to communicate.

Memory Loss

Sometimes, someone with PTSD may start a conversation or make a phone call and suddenly forget the reason for initiating the discussion. Many people may consider this a regular occurrence, but it may be much more than this for those with PTSD.

You may identify this effect as "aphasia," which leads to a difficulty in finding the right words to say or saying something else even when you do know what to say. For those who forget what they intend to say, it is because they lose their train of thought. This may be due to their minds recalling past traumatic events.

Increased Sensitivity

If you have a loved one living with PTSD, you may notice that they often cut off communication abruptly. This is often a result of a hypersensitivity they develop due to PTSD. They will take note of minor details like whether you're listening or the tone of your voice.

For others, this hypersensitivity is in the form of standards they set. When they notice individuals exhibiting traits that fall below their standards, they will choose to cut them off. These standards may include behaviors that depict trustworthiness and avoiding people that breach their trust or betray them.

Trouble Organizing Your Thoughts

PTSD often makes it difficult to organize thoughts in the right way. This makes it almost impossible to deliver your message clearly. For some people, their organized thoughts become jumbled as soon as they get nervous.

When you fail to organize your thoughts, you may end up giving details first before the context. A sudden intrusion of traumatic memories can also cause you to mix up the things you want to say during a conversation.

Inability to Form a Rapport

People only enjoy a conversation once an emotional rapport has been established. PTSD usually causes a lack of affect, which makes it challenging to make this emotional connection. As a result, the conversation may be over sooner than you expect.

Rigidity

Your position on a matter is very important to you, and this makes it difficult for others to change your perspective on a situation. This lack of flexibility usually causes a hindrance during communication. Although it is a way of maintaining control and avoiding danger, it can push others away from you.

Sudden Fight Response

There are times when you may experience an extreme feeling of rage during a conversation, which can bring the discussion to an abrupt end. This is often a negative end by cutting off the other individual or instigating an argument, depending on if the fight response is repressed or expressed.

Struggle Processing Information

After a traumatic event, the way you process information usually changes significantly. You may find out that you're unable to recall all the information in a conversation despite listening intently. There is also a drop in your decision-making capacity.

To help process information more effectively, you may need to take notes. In making the right decisions, you will also need more time to think. This is necessary for you to connect the information and draw a conclusion that makes sense to you.

Difficulty Focusing and Concentrating

When struggling with PTSD, you quickly get distracted during conversations. These distractions may appear in the form of random feelings or thoughts that flood your mind. When this happens, you may need to ask others to repeat what they have said, which can impact the flow of the conversation, moving forward.

Inability to Connect

Effective communication usually requires you to predict the reactions of others, and also see things from their perspective. PTSD can make this a difficult task, since it causes you to become rigid in your views.

You may find it difficult to understand what others are saying, and they might also misunderstand your message. As a result, you feel like an outcast in their world.

How to Develop Good Communication Skills

Living with a loved one who is struggling with PTSD can lead to issues with your interactions and your relationship as a whole. This can make you believe that if they can just find a way to deal with their PTSD, then you can have a happy relationship. You must change this pattern of thinking.

While your partner may experience many benefits by undergoing treatment for PTSD, you also have a part to play in their recovery. Your role is to communicate with your loved one effectively. Even with PTSD treatment, it is common for communication issues to persist.

Remember the following qualities of effective communication:

- It is non-aggressive
- It is understanding and open
- It is respectful

Keeping these in mind, you can go on to establish excellent communication skills. When you communicate effectively, you will notice that your partner will respond appropriately and listen intently. However, establishing effective communication is not as easy as it sounds.

If you say the wrong things, it can result in a response that instigates anger and yelling. When this happens, you may lose sight of your initial goal and also resort to yelling and criticism to convey your point. This can damage the relationship even further.

The following are ways through which you can improve your communication skills.

Picking the Right Time to Talk

Although selecting the right topic for a conversation is crucial, knowing the right time for the discussion is also as important. The emotional state of your loved one can affect the flow and impact of the conversation. A person who is angry or anxious will often not clearly understand the message you're trying to send.

To avoid this outcome, be sure to begin the conversation at the right time. This gives you an opportunity to prepare for the interaction. You decide how you will speak and put more thought into the things you say.

These are some of the best situations for a conversation:

- **When there is enough time:** Effective communication requires time. This will enable you to explain better, and allow your loved one to fully grasp the topic of the conversation.

- **When both parties are calm:** Being calm is necessary. If both parties are calm, then the possibility of the conversation escalating into a heated argument becomes slim.

- **When a good thing happens:** Having a conversation after an event that leaves everyone happy is an excellent idea. Being in a good mood makes it easy to communicate effectively, without the interference of lingering negative thoughts.

- **When both parties are available:** Availability in this instance can refer to free time or readiness. If your loved one isn't ready to talk about a particular topic, then forcing the conversation will only lead to arguments. Agree on a time for the discussion with your loved one if you want to deliver your message effectively.

Changing Your Communication Strategy

Many people experience disappointment due to their communication strategy. You may feel that your loved one should know what to do without you saying it. This includes interpreting for themselves what you want, how you feel, and what you're thinking.

Avoidance is a strategy that you may also adopt. You avoid having conversations because you fear the outcome of the discussion and the response you will get. Developing a new communication strategy will help in achieving effective communication. You can adopt these actions in designing your new approach:

Maintain Positivity

There are surely things you won't like your loved ones doing, but how you express your dislikes matter a lot. Avoid beginning your statements with phrases such as "I hate," "I detest," or "I can't stand."

Be Understanding

When trying to deliver your message, you may end up focusing solely on how you feel. The right approach is also to show an understanding of the feelings of your loved one. Don't let them assume you're trying to criticize or belittle them.

Showing empathy will let them understand that you genuinely care about them and support them. This doesn't imply that you support the behaviors they exhibit.

Be Brief

There is nothing worse than having a conversation seem like a lecture. This is what happens when your statements become too long, so keep them as short as possible.

This will give your partner opportunities to respond and contribute to the conversation.

Focus on the Present

A conversation that focuses on the past will likely only cause your loved one to get defensive. Don't bring up any problem, argument, or behavior from the past. You want them to move on from past trauma, and this is a way to help.

"I" Statements are the Best

When you replace words like 'your' with 'I,' you can avoid making your statements seem like accusations. A statement like "I am worried about you when you scream in your sleep" is much better than saying, "Your constant screaming at night makes it difficult for me to sleep comfortably."

Learning to use "I" statements will help prevent your loved ones from getting defensive or ending the conversation.

Developing your communication skills will be a massive help if you want to address issues in your relationships more effectively. Although PTSD usually makes communication tough, you must always remember the following:

- Listen
- Develop and stick to your communication strategy
- Pay attention to how you speak
- Pick the right time for the conversation

There are certain areas treatment for PTSD won't impact. Effective communication is a strategy to help overturn the effect of PTSD in your relationship, and it is a skill that can improve your daily life.

The practice is also necessary for making your new communication strategy a part of you. Doing so regularly will help you become an effective listener in addition to being effective as a speaker.

Interacting Correctly with Loved Ones

There are many ways to interact with loved ones struggling with PTSD. Simple actions like listening without being judgmental, bringing food, offering hugs, being helpful around the house, and being present are all necessary. These are actions that can speak louder than your words.

You must never try to fix your partner. Don't mention anything about how long recovery should take, or how they need to get back to being 'normal' quickly. They are the ones that feel the most impact of their PTSD.

Your role is to be their rock in this trying time. Although this can be difficult, building a support group can help. If you understand all these, then you need to learn about the right ways to phrase your questions and comments you shouldn't make.

Phrasing Questions

Developing your communication skills is just a step toward your overall goal. To interact successfully with someone struggling with PTSD, you must learn how to phrase questions correctly. This will enable you to get the response you desire regarding their condition.

Depending on your phrasing, your question will fall into one of three categories:

- Open-ended questions
- Closed questions
- Leading questions

During your interaction with your loved ones, be sure to make use of open-ended questions. The following are some characteristics of open-ended questions:

- There is no hidden suggestion, emotional charge, or assumption
- They help in discovering new opinions and feelings on a subject matter
- They are useful in gaining more information about another individual
- They are questions that require more than one-word answers
- Answering these questions requires thought and reflection

When you use open-ended questions, you are telling your loved one that you genuinely want to communicate with them. They help create a form of understanding and cooperation between you and your partner.

The following are examples of open-ended questions:

- How do you feel about your new boss?
- What was your experience at the gym like?
- What are your thoughts on the new house?
- Can you tell me more about the problem?

In contrast, the following closed questions will get a different kind of answer:

- Do you like your new boss?
- Was the event too long?

Talking to Someone with PTSD

In addition to the way you phrase questions, you should also think carefully about what you say during a conversation. Certain statements you make can help them relax and conclude that you truly care about them. The following are simple statements and how your loved one can interpret them:

- "I want us to watch a movie instead of going out to a large gathering."

This implies that you know they can't handle being in a large crowd at the moment, but that you also understand they don't want to be alone.

- "I think you're amazing, and I love you."

This is a way to spread positivity and reassure them that you don't blame them or think of them as a burden. People with PTSD need to hear this often.

- "I know you may not feel like stepping out, but we would love for you to come hang out with us."

The first part of this statement eliminates the need for your loved one to come up with an excuse for not coming. The second part shows that you always have them in your thoughts.

- "I'm going to stay around a little longer. I'm worried you might hurt yourself."

Although they may never say it, many people with PTSD tend to worry about this, so they appreciate your company.

- "I want to understand you better, so I am going to learn as much as I can about your condition."

This shows that you really care about them.

- "Let me do the dishes while you do the things that matter to you."

Sometimes, housework can be stressful for people with PTSD. If you notice your loved one is spending a lot of time in bed or still wearing their pajamas, then offer a helping hand.

- "I am here for you, always."

You're not giving deadlines or pressuring your loved ones into doing anything. This is a show of support.

Things You Shouldn't Say to Your Loved One

In dealing with PTSD, there are several other things your loved one struggles with. These include crowds, flashing lights, and loud noises, which can trigger PTSD symptoms. They may also have to deal with people who make rude comments regarding their condition.

You mustn't add to their problems. Knowing some of the insensitive comments people make can help you avoid making the same mistake.

"Shouldn't you be over it already?"

When you make this comment, you're giving the impression that people should overcome PTSD after a specific period. In reality, this is not the case. For many people, they don't even discover the disorder until long after the event has occurred.

Dealing with PTSD triggers can often be a lifelong struggle. Despite the availability of treatments such as therapy and medications, the healing process takes months or years to complete.

"How many people did you kill?"

If your loved one is a veteran, then this is one question you must try not to ask. If they feel comfortable talking to you about it, they will. Don't try to force out more information than they are willing to give.

Feelings of shame and guilt are common among people who have PTSD. Most veterans feel guilty when they think about those they couldn't save and being alive while others aren't. You can unknowingly trigger these feelings by asking this question.

When you question the traumatic experiences of your loved ones, it seems like you're trying to downplay the significance of the trauma. This can make them feel less secure.

"My supervisor screamed at me today. I may have PTSD now."

Making jokes to ease the tension in your home or relationship is a good idea, but you must never make jokes about this illness. You can hurt your loved one more when you do this.

Developing PTSD often occurs when you go through a life-threatening event, such as war, a car crash, or rape. A bad day at work or getting scolded by your boss will never lead to PTSD.

"You're surely a veteran since you have PTSD."

This comment is a form of generalization. First, you should understand that not all veterans have PTSD. Second, not everyone who has PTSD has been in any type of military conflict.

Natural disasters, rape, robbery, mass shootings, death of a loved one, terrorism, and road accidents are some events that may lead to PTSD. Making comments that show your ignorance can cause your loved one to feel shame.

"Surprise!"

Please, don't do this to anyone who has PTSD. They are constantly looking out for threats, so surprise parties and sneaking up on them will startle them easily. This is a result of hypervigilance, which they develop as a symptom of PTSD.

For veterans, hypervigilance is a necessity for survival. When these veterans leave the battlefield, this becomes a cause of panic, paranoia, and other PTSD reactions. You may also notice these reactions when they experience sudden physical contact.

"Why are you always edgy?"

The way people with PTSD react to certain situations can make them appear uptight. What they need is for you to respect their space, and do so without judging. Being uptight, jittery, or edgy isn't an option—it is a symptom of PTSD.

Despite undergoing treatment for the disorder, it is common for these symptoms to appear suddenly. In place of this comment, you can simply respond with "I'm sorry" anytime you notice these sudden reactions. The reaction may be to an action or a statement you've made.

Power of Affirmative Phrases

What you say to yourself has a significant impact on the way you act, think, and feel. Also, these have a direct effect on your mental health. In their quest for healing, your loved one must speak these positive affirmations.

Despite the importance of positivity in the healing process, it is often difficult for a person who has PTSD to repeat positive affirmations. Their thoughts are usually clouded by negativity. To address this issue, you must take time to 'rewire' their thoughts.

Shame, guilt, and negative self-talk are some of the outcomes of past trauma. They are wounds buried deep inside, in places where medication can never reach. You can help your loved one notice wounds and heal them through positivity.

Through positive affirmations, people can improve their health physically, mentally, and emotionally. In crafting positive statements to use with your loved one, there is one thing you must always remember. This is the fact that you need to put them first.

What this means is that you must never refer to them using a group term—for example, language like "the retarded," "the dumb," and other collective ways of referring to people with disabilities. When talking about someone with PTSD, never use the phrase "afflicted by PTSD."

You can say, "a person who has PTSD," instead. The idea is to show individuality, dignity, and equality in the way you describe them.

These positive statements can boost the spirits of your loved one:

- It was never your fault.
- I'm always here to listen if you're willing to talk.
- I love and cherish you.
- You don't deserve what happened to you, and it should have never happened.
- I believe you.
- Together, we can make it through this.
- You're a good person.
- Is there any way I can help you feel safe?
- I want you to know you are not alone.
- You're not a bad person for feeling angry or hurt.
- You're in extreme pain, and that is the reason for your sudden emotional breakdowns. You were not being selfish.
- I am sorry for the things that happened to you.
- I am so proud of the progress you've made.

- Never feel like you're alone, regardless of what you see around you.
- I admire and respect you for the way you're handling things.
- It isn't something you could have stopped. You're not weak or wrong.
- I am always here to help if you need me, don't hesitate to call me for any reason.
- Thank you for being a survivor.
- Don't be afraid to tell me what you need, I will understand.

In addition to this, you should also remember the following:

- Always listen to what your loved one has to say.
- You must show understanding, patience, and support.
- Be sure to relax.
- It is good to offer assistance, but don't feel bad if you're turned down and never insist on your offer.
- Due to the factors that influence PTSD symptoms, you should expect challenging times as well as periods of comfort and ease.
- There are times when you don't have the right answer—saying "let me check" or "I don't know" are suitable options.

Chapter 6:

Don't Neglect Yourself

Offering constant support to your loved one through their recovery requires a lot of energy and can be stressful. When you continuously see someone you love battling with an issue, it can be difficult and distressing.

In many situations, you can offer support without it affecting you personally. But when the support and stress are almost never-ending, it can lead to caregiver burden.

Caregiver Burden: What Does It Mean?

PTSD can be a very destructive illness, and the individual with PTSD may need to be continuously cared for by someone close to them. This is usually a partner, parent, or other family members.

As a partner of an individual living with PTSD, you may deal with numerous stressors that come with caring for someone with this condition. Some of these stressors include dealing with the PTSD symptoms, financial inconvenience, and loss of intimacy.

Often, the only people who may be available to deal with these stressors are the partners. This can be extremely tedious for them alone, and due to this, they may experience a tremendous amount of stress and strain—or caregiver burden.

Studies on Caregiver Burden

Numerous studies have observed caregiver burden among partners caring for those they love with PTSD.

In the first study, researchers observed 154 spouses of veterans who have PTSD. They realized that the seriousness of the PTSD symptoms of the veterans was linked to the level of distress and caregiver burden the spouse experienced.

As the PTSD symptoms of the spouse worsened, the amount of distress and caregiver burden faced by the partner increased, as well.

Researchers also observed how symptoms of PTSD, like violence, depression, and anger, affect relationships with caregivers and spouses with PTSD. There may be a link between the level of detail the partner with PTSD shared with their spouse; however, more research needs to be done to understand these problems better.

Studies into the spouses of combat veterans also observed that this stress could have damaging psychological consequences. In the wives of veterans with PTSD, there is a higher risk of symptoms like panic disorder, enhanced suicidal tendencies, generalized anxiety disorder, and clinical depression.

Signs of Caregiver Burden

Helping others heal from suffering requires empathy and compassion. The emotional connections we create with others can often leave us facing distress of our own. This is common when dealing with various conditions, including PTSD.

Caregiver burden can result in symptoms which are a little similar to PTSD like:

- Poor sleep
- Isolation
- Forgetfulness
- Failure to exercise
- Inability to care for oneself when sick
- Ignoring medical appointments of your own
- Anxiety and depression
- Headaches
- Increase or reduction in food intake
- Thoughts of self-harm or of harming the individual being cared for

- Disinterest in activities you used to enjoy

Caregivers also face the danger of developing a dependence on substances, alcohol, and tobacco as a means of coping with all of the feelings that come with their responsibility. Even though caring for someone you love is something that shows commitment, it can cause a considerable amount of stress.

Caregivers have a higher likelihood to suffer from chronic illnesses, as well, including high blood pressure and high cholesterol levels. According to studies, an estimate of no less than 59 percent of caregivers suffer from clinical depression.

If we start to abandon our own needs or ignore ourselves while taking care of others, we can put our health and overall well-being in danger. There are a few things you can do to ensure this does not happen to you. One significant way to do this is to practice good self-care.

Preventing Caregiver Burden

Develop Emotional Boundaries

To care for someone who is trying to heal from trauma, you will need to be emotionally involved. Also, you will have to show commitment and empathy as a caregiver.

These traits will help you better understand what the person is going through and help you stick through the situation. However, these good traits can also drag you down if you become excessively involved.

It is best to establish healthy boundaries between you and the loved one you are trying to help, which will prevent you from carrying their experiences and pain as yours. This can be extremely difficult, particularly if it is someone you love and have spent so much time with over the years.

You will need to learn to stay connected while also remembering that you are a person with your own needs. Being aware in this manner will help you maintain the required space between you as the caregiver and the individual you are trying to help.

Develop a Support Network

Similar to how a good support network can help someone with PTSD, it can also be beneficial to you as a caregiver. A good support network can aid in reducing stress reactions in a caregiver.

A good support network can also teach you as a caregiver what you need to know about PTSD and the various symptoms it brings. By identifying these symptoms and why they arise, you can better understand why your loved one is acting the way they are and how to handle it.

Having a good support network can get you past the stress and strike the much-needed balance between helping and hurting. You can seek social support from your friends, colleagues, and family members; however, you need to ensure you are getting support from the appropriate outlets. If your support system is draining you instead of uplifting you, then it may cause more harm than good.

As a caregiver, you can also benefit from attending support groups or individual therapy. There, you can learn how to cope with the PTSD symptoms of your loved one. You can also benefit from couples counseling.

Recently, there has been a rise in online groups, which allows caregivers of people with PTSD to collaborate. If you do decide to go the online route, be sure to connect with individuals who are experiencing the same challenges as you but are still able to offer the support you need.

Minimize Stress from Work

Research shows a strong link between high levels of work stress and levels of psychological distress and other symptoms of caregiver burden. Stress from work can be very exhausting, and depending on the kind of job involved, it can take a huge chunk away from our stamina. When this happens, it leaves you more vulnerable to the stress that comes with being a caregiver for someone with PTSD.

To curb this, make adjustments at work whenever you can to reduce the level of stress you are exposed to. You can request days off here and there, giving your body time to relax and build up lost energy.

If you are acting as a caregiver for your spouse, it may be beneficial to accept offers from people who can help take the pressure off you. Also, do your best to make sure your home is relaxing and offers you the energy you need, instead of further depleting you.

Leverage Active Coping Measures

Every one of us copes with stressful situations differently. The coping measure we choose can have a huge impact on our stress levels. According to researchers Schauben and Frazier, individuals who used active coping measures did not report as many symptoms of caregiver burden.

Examples of active coping measures are social support, humor, and planning your schedule and time. Other experts have warned against the use of avoidant or negative coping mechanisms like the use of substances, alcohol, and others. It has been observed that these are linked with trauma symptoms among caregivers.

Be Self-Aware

Being self-aware means paying attention to our thoughts and actions. This way, we can observe the way we interact with others and the way our body feels in general. Self-awareness can help you determine the level of stress you are dealing with each day, so you can work toward reducing it.

It can also help you determine when you need to focus on yourself more. There are many ways to develop self-awareness, such as:

- Reading
- Having discussions with others
- Journaling
- Meditation and other similar activities
- Counseling, and so on.

It may seem like a lot of effort to cultivate self-awareness. However, having this capacity can help you deal with all of the stressors that come from caregiving before it causes serious damage to your life.

Practicing Self-Care

Self-care, as the name implies, simply means caring for one's self. As stated above, it can be easy for a caregiver to ignore their own needs and give priority to the person they are trying to care for.

However, doing this does more harm than good, and to make certain that you don't experience a caregiver burden, there are some ways you can care for yourself.

Take Frequent Breaks

If you are caring for someone that needs your attention most of the time, it will be beneficial to take frequent breaks. Ensure you take no less than 30 minutes break once or twice daily. If possible, request the help of another close family member or friend to relieve you while you get yourself together.

Regardless of how much time you schedule for your break, be certain you spend it doing something just for you. Do something you enjoy—see a movie, take a nap, or get a massage. Also, when you take this break, try to talk about other things that don't have to do with the PTSD symptoms your loved one is experiencing.

Exercise

It can be very difficult to work out when the goal is to refill your energy. However, this is one of the best self-care tips available. Working out can help lift your mood and make you feel better about yourself.

When working out, choose something light. This does not mean you have to lift the largest weights you can find, or run for hours non-stop. Instead, moderate exercise can be of help. If you have the capacity, try to ensure your workout takes place outside, so that the sun and fresh air can help make you feel energized.

If the weather is not favorable, you can try out yoga and fitness applications, which you can set up from the comfort of your home. Try not to engage in excessively stressful workouts when you're already dealing with stress. Rather, pursue less intensive activities like dancing, walking, or Tai Chi.

Consume a Balanced Diet

Eating meals with the right proportions of nutrients is one of the best ways to maintain your overall energy and health. A great way to go about this is to eat only whole foods.

When you replace processed meals and added sugars with vegetables, soup, and lean protein, you will instantly start to notice the changes in your body. There are numerous resources available on the Internet which will provide you with nutritious meal recipes. There will certainly be healthy options available for you regardless of your preference.

Pay Attention to Your Health

Many caregivers make the mistake of ignoring their health. This may result in them falling ill or getting injured. If you feel you are starting to get sick, it is best to take some rest.

If you injure yourself, prioritize getting yourself back into shape. You can only care for your loved one when you are also of good health.

Pamper Yourself

Sometimes, all you need is to treat yourself in a manner that makes you fulfilled. Good options include getting a manicure, massage, or spending time at your favorite restaurant or park. Do anything that makes you happy and satisfied.

Be certain to reward yourself frequently for the wonderful way you are helping your loved one. Don't feel guilty about treating yourself, because you deserve every bit of it.

Get Adequate Sleep

When you are busy, it is very easy to ignore sleep. Caring for a loved one who has PTSD can be extremely time-consuming and may bite into your sleep time. This is particularly the case for those who experience nightmares and other symptoms that keep them awake at night.

What's more, some caregivers don't have good sleep routines. This, combined with other stressors one might experience, can make it extremely difficult to get the right amount of sleep. It is recommended that adults get no less than seven or eight hours of sleep each day to maintain good health.

To ensure you are not shaving off part of your sleep time, try to develop a great sleep routine. Schedule your sleep time so that you can wake and go to bed at the same time every day.

Another option could be to take a warm bath and read a book before bedtime. Try to turn off all your electronics an hour before bedtimes, as the light rays from these gadgets may prevent you from getting the quality sleep you need.

Also, avoid eating huge meals or consuming alcohol before you go to bed and turn off all the lights in your room to ensure it is cool and dark. Lights can interrupt your sleep, so you want to make sure that you turn them all off before you go to bed.

Keep in Touch With Friends

Trying to get your loved one into good shape and help them recover can take up all of your time. This may result in you inadvertently isolating yourself from your friends.

However, this can do more harm than good. Try to schedule some time to stay connected with your friends. Good friends can put a smile on your face and provide you with the support you need to get you through the stressful process.

Connecting with friends helps your brain produce oxytocin, which is a hormone that helps prevent an increase in stress hormones and help you stay calm. Even if you can't physically hang out with your friends, make sure you take time to call or send mails as frequently as you can.

Laugh

When you spend all your time listening to the experience of a loved one who has suffered from trauma, it can start to rub off on you, too. For this reason, you will need to hold on to your sense of humor to keep you in the right shape.

To do this, watch a funny movie or comedy. You can also read humorous books or hang around people that make you laugh. Also, checking your social platforms can provide you with a constant source of humor each day. There are tons of funny pages to follow on Facebook and Instagram.

What's more, you can even share some of this humor with your loved one. This is sure to be a relief, considering the PTSD symptoms they may be experiencing.

Go Outside

There are times when leaving your home and doing something as simple as taking a walk or paying a visit to your favorite park can be all you need to feel great.

You can go by yourself or meet up with a friend to enjoy the company. The feeling of fresh air and sunlight on your skin can help re-energize you and brighten your day. Going outside can help you see that the world does have great things to offer.

Focus on a Single Task

Concentrate on one specific thing at a time and let yourself know that you can create something amazing and positive. The feeling of fulfillment that comes with completing daily activities is enough to boost your day.

Stay Away from the Media

After continually listening to the traumatic experience of your loved one dealing with PTSD, it can begin to rub off on you. If you also consume media that brings about negative news, you will only feel worse.

Much of the news we read in the media is usually about disasters, or false images that we may compare ourselves with. Take a break from these sources and instead focus on the good things going on in your life.

This is one of the easiest and most beneficial self-care techniques anybody can incorporate into their lives.

Mindful Breathing

Meditation and other mindful breathing techniques are some of the most rewarding activities anybody can engage in. Meditating disconnects you from every stressor and negative vibe in your life, allowing you to focus your mind on yourself and the present moment. Doing this for as little as five minutes each day can make a considerable difference.

It is an opportunity to heal your mind and soul, so you have the capacity to continue caring for your loved ones and others around you.

Try this mindful breathing exercise anytime you feel stressed:

- Find a comfortable environment and relax. Take a deep breath.
- Next, take note of the sounds in your environment and let them stay where they are. Be aware of everything around you, while you take in slow, deep breaths and release them at the same pace.
- Close your eyes, and free yourself from all of your concerns. This should feel like letting go of a huge stone you have been hauling around.

Doing this will let you move away from the worries you carry.

- Pay attention to your breath. Let yourself feel all of the sensations and awareness that come with it. Feel the cool air you are taking in and the warm air leaving. Also, feel your belly expand and contract, as well as your chest rising and falling. Let go of control and allow your breath to flow in and out as it desires.

- Begin to softly count your breaths. You can count from one to five, and repeat it once you are done. At this point, your mind may start to drift. This is not abnormal—when this happens, all you need to do is start counting once more.

- Pay more attention to your breathing, and the moment your mind settles down during the first few minutes, you will realize it becomes easier to channel your attention to the air as it goes into your lungs and out once more.

- Now, revert your focus to your present thoughts. Be aware of these thoughts and let yourself know that you are aware of them.

- Don't fall into the temptation of getting distracted by these thoughts—however, it's best not to struggle with them either. Your goal is to be with your thoughts without getting distracted. Anytime you see yourself being drawn in by these thoughts, repeat the process once more.

- Lastly, feel the sense of peace that grows inside you as you continue to breathe. Once you have gotten to this state, you may choose to remain there for as long as you desire.
- Then, open your eyes, stretch, and get up.

Regular Journaling

Writing down your thoughts on paper can be very therapeutic. As mentioned, continually hearing the details of the trauma your loved one experienced can affect you, too. You begin to think about the details of the event until they start to impact your own life.

Sometimes, all you need to do to find some peace within your head is to write down those thoughts. When you do, you feel free. You don't need to continuously allow them to take up space in your mind. Putting them in a journal can minimize these thoughts and help you feel better.

The great part about journaling is that you can do it anywhere. You can write in the comfort of your home or even while on the move. Every time you feel your head is going to explode due to all of the thoughts, write them down!

Purchase a portable journal to ensure you can carry it about with ease without being inconvenienced, or use an app that will always be available on your phone.

To journal in the right manner, the following can be of help:

- **Write Without Restrictions**: Write down everything you want without holding anything back. Don't think about what you are writing—just write. This is your free place, and there won't be anyone to judge you, so make certain you are writing freely.

  Doing this will help you put down those feelings and thoughts you never realized existed in the first place. If you need help with this, you can write about how your life is going presently. Describe your workplace and how it is at home, caring for your loved one. The better your understanding of where you are presently, the easier it will be to write.

- **Stay Consistent**: Write as often as possible. You can write for a few minutes or more, depending on how much time you are willing to invest in this. You might want to set up a timer to help you keep track; however, your objective should not be the amount you write but how consistent you can be with this. You may want to keep track of how your loved one's condition has been affecting you or things that have made you angry. There are instances where it may feel like you don't have so much to write, but that's fine—just be consistent.

After you have gotten accustomed to writing a few minutes each day, it will become a habit, and you can invest more time if you desire. If you observe that you are no longer as consistent as before, you may want to cut down the time into something that you can handle.

- **Take a Break**: After you have put down all of your feelings, take a brief break. It can be exhausting to deal with all of these emotions brewing in your mind and writing them down. To make this work, have a timer in place and stop writing as soon as you have exhausted the allocated time. Then, take a break as soon as you are done.

- **Review Your Journal Monthly**: At the end of each month, go through everything you have written in your journal. Observe anything that may have changed in your life and note down what has improved and what has not. You may also notice small wins that you did not notice previously, which can become a basis of satisfaction and happiness for you.

Reduce Noise from Your Life

Noise is everywhere in our environments. This could be someone telling you that you are not good enough, or someone trying to drag you into speaking ill about another close acquaintance. It could also be images or shows, making you feel the wrong way about yourself.

Be strategic about the thoughts that you let in. You have a choice to free yourself from conversations that don't make you feel good. You can also leave environments that don't offer you any benefit.

In order to reduce some of this noise for self-care, you can do the following:

- Set boundaries with people, especially those who want to drag you into toxic conversations.
- Invest in some quality earplugs which can help you keep out noise. This is particularly useful in situations where you can't turn off the noise, like in a public setting.

Controlling what goes into your mind is one of the best forms of self-care you can engage in. What you let in can either cause you harm or empower you.

Say No Frequently

Another amazing self-care practice anyone can leverage is to say "no." If you are not in the mood to do something, just say no. You have the right to.

Perhaps you notice that your loved one is starting to take advantage of you. In that instance, you are allowed to say no, as well.

Regardless of the situation, thing, or individual that makes you feel unhappy, you have the right to say no as much as you want.

Is Self-Care Selfish?

As someone who is caring for a loved one with PTSD, it can be easy to feel guilt when you do take some time to care for yourself.

This is one of the primary reasons why many caregivers fail to care for themselves until they end up with caregiver burden.

Why, then, does this happen? Why do you feel selfish for taking some time for self-care?

Scheduling time for yourself and prioritizing self-care means you are taking time off other things that you are currently engaged in, like your relationships and your loved one with PTSD. People who are affected by this may be unhappy about it and might make you feel guilty. It is our concern for the way other people react that actually makes us feel selfish.

While you may feel that your desire to take time off for self-care is selfish, this is not the case. Caring for yourself is crucial, but it's still one of the most frequently ignored things for many caregivers.

However, this should not be the case because when you care for your needs, the loved one you care for will benefit, too. In essence, the care you offer for yourself is the care you will offer to those you love.

It does not benefit you to care for others constantly and end up getting sick. Caring for yourself each day is, in the long run, the best way you can care for those you love. You need to take time off to recharge because living with and caring for people who have PTSD can be very distressing and stressful.

As opposed to other, more temporary mental conditions, PTSD can sometimes last for an extremely long time. This is why, as a caregiver, you need to schedule some time to rest and re-energize.

The more you learn how to care for yourself as a caregiver, the better you will be able to care for your loved one and others.

Conclusion

PTSD is a severe condition that can be destructive to your relationship. But you can educate yourself about this condition and help your loved one overcome it with the help of the information collected in this book.

Don't forget; this is not something that will happen in a day. It needs commitment, effort, and understanding on your part as the caregiver to deal with all of the PTSD symptoms your loved one may experience.

It also requires commitment and effort on the part of your loved one, as well, or getting the treatment they seek will be almost impossible.

PTSD manifests in your relationship through various symptoms, as we covered in chapter one. As a recap, some of these include:

- Flashbacks,
- Nightmares,
- Isolation and withdrawal,
- Anxiety,
- Hypersensitivity,
- Depression,

- Anger outbursts, and so on.

Even with all of these, it is possible to get treatment, and you can encourage your loved one to look at all of the options available. Some of the common ones are:

- Cognitive Processing Therapy (CPT)
- Prolonged Exposure Therapy
- Eye Movement Desensitization and Reprocessing (EMDR)
- Stress Inoculation Training (SIT)
- Medications

You can also help your loved one to recover by providing them with support. As the loved one of a person living with PTSD, you can provide support by:

- Understanding, anticipating, and managing their triggers.
- Respecting their personal space.
- Watching out for warning signs.
- Remaining positive.
- Dealing with all of their anger, irritability, and volatility.
- Knowing when to get medical assistance.

However, you also need to exercise caution when trying to support your loved one. It can be easy to ignore your own needs and develop caregiver burden. The symptoms of a caregiver burden are similar to that of PTSD:

- Poor sleep
- Isolation
- Forgetfulness
- Failure to exercise
- Inability to care for oneself when sick
- Ignoring medical appointments of your own
- Anxiety and depression

To curb this, there are some things you can do:

- Create emotional boundaries;
- Establish a good support network;
- Practice good self-care by eating healthy, getting adequate sleep, working out, and meditating, among others.

Even though it may feel selfish to take time off to engage in self-care, it is not. It is best to take care of yourself because if your health is in a bad state, you won't be able to care for anyone else. Worse still, you may fall ill and end up with a mini trauma instead.

Lastly, communication is key if you plan to maintain your relationship with your loved one. PTSD can affect communication in a relationship through the following ways:

- Difficulty in organizing information
- Inability to open up
- Memory problems
- Lack of focus and concentration
- Sense of disconnect
- Anger

You will need to prepare for all of this and learn how to properly communicate with your partner if you want them to recover. For instance, you should not minimize or trivialize their issue.

What's more, you need to be non-judgmental and should not compare them to other people you know. Everyone experiences and reacts to trauma differently, and your goal should be there for them instead of making them feel worse.

Regardless of how much control PTSD has over your loved one and your relationship, there is still hope. You deserve happiness, and if you strive toward it, you will certainly achieve it.

Also, as you spend time with and care for your loved one, you will most likely have mixed feelings. Sometimes, these could be positive feelings, and other times, your feelings may be negative. This does not mean you are a terrible person. You're only human, and you need to accept both feelings—with time, the negative ones will pass.

I am not assuring you that there won't be step-backs during this journey. But what I can promise is that if you use all of the information I have incorporated into this book the right way, you can help free your loved one from their frustrating PTSD symptoms.

I sincerely hope that you get all you wish for once you are through with this book. I see your relationship going to greater heights as you save the person you love and help them get their life back on track.

Thank you for allowing me to guide you through this hurdle with my experience. If you found this book helpful to you or someone you know, do leave a positive review.

References

(n.d.). Retrieved from https://www.apa.org/ptsd-guideline/treatments/prolonged-exposure

Bressert, S. (2018, December 26). How Does PTSD Affect Relationships? Retrieved from https://psychcentral.com/lib/ptsd-and-relationships/

Bressert, S. (2018, December 26). How Does PTSD Affect Relationships? Retrieved from https://psychcentral.com/lib/ptsd-and-relationships/

Gardner, A., & Gardner, A. (2017, October 30). 7 Things You Should Never Say to Someone With PTSD. Retrieved from https://www.health.com/condition/ptsd/ptsd-what-not-to-say

Gardner, A., & Gardner, A. (2017, October 30). 7 Things You Should Never Say to Someone With PTSD. Retrieved from https://www.health.com/condition/ptsd/ptsd-what-not-to-say

Helping someone with PTSD. (n.d.). Retrieved from https://www.ptsduk.org/friends-and-family/helping-someone-with-ptsd/

Helping Someone with PTSD. (2020, February 17). Retrieved from https://www.helpguide.org/articles/ptsd-trauma/helping-someone-with-ptsd.htm

How to Help Someone with PTSD. (2015, July 1). Retrieved from https://lotsahelpinghands.com/blog/how-to-help-someone-with-ptsd/

Lotherington, F. (n.d.). Self-care is not selfish. Retrieved from https://www.unimedliving.com/self-care/what-is-self-care/self-care-is-not-selfish.html

Lotherington, F. (n.d.). Self-care is not selfish. Retrieved from https://www.unimedliving.com/self-care/what-is-self-care/self-care-is-not-selfish.html

Maynard, E. (2020, January 13). Correlation Between Structures of the Brain Function and PTSD. Retrieved from https://www.verywellmind.com/what-exactly-does-ptsd-do-to-the-brain-2797210

PTSD Challenges – Communication. (n.d.). Retrieved from http://www.new-synapse.com/aps/wordpress/?p=1614

Seton, A. (2017, July 7). How Cognitive Processing Therapy Works to Treat PTSD. Retrieved from https://www.seton.net/behavioral-health-care/2017/07/07/cognitive-processing-therapy-works-treat-ptsd/

Tartakovsky, M. (2018, October 8). How Clinicians Practice Self-Care & 9 Tips for Readers. Retrieved from https://psychcentral.com/lib/how-clinicians-practice-self-care-9-tips-for-readers/

Made in the USA
Columbia, SC
05 July 2020

13327236R00093